FROM OFF ISLAND

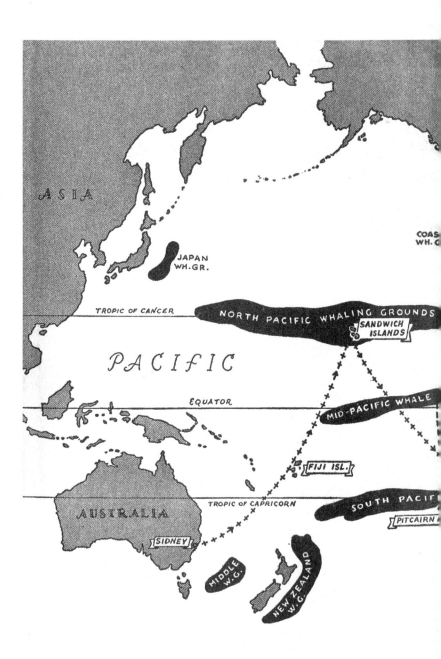

LEGEND
+ + + + + Grandmother's First Voyage + + +
− − − − − Her Five Year Whaling Voyage − −
Sperm Whaling Grounds

NORTH

SAN FRANCISCO

AMERICA

CALIF.
WH.GR.

ATLANTIC

MARTHA'S
VINYARD

AZORES

AZORES   WH.GR.

OCEAN

GALAPAGOS

OFF SHORE
WHALE
GR.

TUMBES
PAITA

SOUTH

AMERICA

WHALING GROUNDS

OFF SHORE WH. GR.

TALCAHUANO

JUAN FERNANDEZ
ISLAND

OCEA

AF

CAPE
HORN

MARY CARLIN

From off Island

THE STORY OF MY GRANDMOTHER

BY DIONIS COFFIN RIGGS

in collaboration with

SIDNEY NOYES RIGGS

Whittlesey House

McGRAW-HILL BOOK COMPANY, INC.

New York · London

Facsimile Edition
Copyright © 1993, Cleaveland House Books

Cover Design by The Tisbury Printer, Martha's Vineyard
Printing by Walsworth Publishing Company

Second Facsimile Edition
Copyright © 2016, Cleaveland House Books

Cover Design, by Elizabeth Whelan, Cuttyhunk Island

Depiction of Mary Carlin Cleaveland being rowed
ashore from the whaling ship *Seconet* captained by her husband
James Freeman Cleaveland of West Tisbury, Massachusetts

Printing by The Tisbury Printer, Martha's Vineyard, MA

PUBLISHED BY WHITTLESEY HOUSE
A division of the McGraw-Hill Book Company, Inc.

Printed in the United States of America by the Maple Press Co., York, Pa.

TO

Alvida, Ann and Cynthia

Acknowledgments

IN WRITING this book we have had help from many sources—primarily from the person most concerned in living the story—Grandmother herself. Her daughters, Alvida, Henrietta, and Mary Wilder, have been of great assistance with stories of their parents and grandparents and of the old days that they heard about as children.

Their memories have been reinforced by those of other relatives and neighbors in West Tisbury: Mrs. E. Warren Foote, Donald Campbell, Miss Elizabeth Cleaveland, Mrs. H. C. Sullivan, Mrs. Raymond Walker, the members of several Look families, Miss Laura Lee, Mr. and Mrs. Johnson Whiting, Mrs. Herbert Burt, Mrs. David Mayhew, Mrs. Dana Hancock, Mr. and Mrs. George G. Gifford, Ulysses E. Mayhew, and others. We appreciate their contribution.

Very important was the fact that we were able to verify so much of the material by going through the old files of the *Vineyard Gazette*. We thank the editors, Mr. and Mrs. Henry Beetle Hough, for that privilege.

To the many customshouse officials, secretaries of South American consulates, librarians, and custodians of museums, to whom we have appealed, we extend thanks for their courtesy in sending us information, or in helping us find it.

We are indebted to Donald Campbell and Joseph Chase Allen for checking on the whaling scenes, and to several good friends for criticism.

And finally we wish to thank those who have made the work easier by their interest and encouragement during the progress of the book.

DIONIS COFFIN RIGGS
SIDNEY NOYES RIGGS

Contents

Illustrations

Prologue

THOSE who know Martha's Vineyard only as a summer resort may still be able to picture it as a whaling
center whose busy ports used to be swarming with activity. Vessels cleared from Edgartown and Holmes's Hole
for foreign lands—or for no land at all—just whaling for
four or five years. Drays bearing supplies and casks of
water rumbled along the well-worn streets. Above
the houses tall masts stood up with their rigging outlined
against the sky. Laboring men worked late, and sailors
led a merry life in port.

It was then that the captains' houses were built in
rows along the waterfront, each one topped with a lookout, each simple in design like a fine ship. They stand as
sturdy today.

The sea blood seeped back into the interior—to West
Tisbury, and "up-island" into Chilmark. There, too,
the captains built great houses that commanded the

countryside. They bought fast horses and did a little farming. But they soon went back to sea again, taking their sons and their neighbors' sons with them.

Most of the women stayed at home to bear children a Cape Horn voyage apart. They'd knit, and talk, and watch for letters—and worry whenever the wind blew loudly and the surf moaned against the South Shore.

But Grandmother, coming "from off island," was different.

BOOK I

The Island

SPRING, 1852

I

The New Bedford Mercury, May 14, 1852:
"No arrivals. Wind N.E., a gale."

THE ocean had been growling for days. The breakers
pounded against the south side, withdrew with a hissing, sucking sound, then beat again and again and again.
It could be heard inland as far as the center of the
island. Farther north it became a dull, heavy throb
that drummed monotonously.

Yesterday the roar had almost died away. Clouds
seemed to blanket the sound. Then a little spitting rain
hit against the northeast windows. A pair of robins hurried back and forth from the barnyard to the apple
orchard with bits of mud and straw, trying to get their
nest built before the storm set in. The rain slashed down
harder. The wind rose. By morning the daffodils were
beaten flat against the ground.

3

Tonight the rain had almost stopped, and the wind let up. The house felt warm with a good fire in the kitchen stove. The wall flashed back reflections of the fire.

Mrs. Henry Cleaveland sat by the stove rocking. The girls had gone to bed, but she was in no mood for sleep. She couldn't even sit still for long. The storm was by no means over, for the wind had "backed around." This was one of those lulls that would precede a more furious onslaught. She took up the whaleoil lamp and, going to the stove, lighted the wick with a twisted paper. She put the light on the shelf near the window, where it burned with a calm, white flame, wavering only a little as she moved about.

Then, as she had expected, more rain came. It started gently—demurely pattering on the little new leaves. It became insistent. It pounded and drummed against the glass panes. Wind whirled around the corners of the house, driving the rain against the shingles. The apple blossoms would be whipped off the trees.

Mrs. Cleaveland took another lamp, lighted it, and went into the dining room. This place was sheltered from the northeast, so that it seemed quiet. But the listening woman could hear the rain sloshing into the big pools that two days of wet weather had formed over the already soaked earth. She could hear the wind swishing through the air, bowing the branches, but it didn't beat against the windows here.

Picking up her shawl, she went into the front room. It had been shut up all winter, for there had been no funerals, no weddings, not even a knitting bee since last fall. Her best furniture stood out with dignity. The

4

prints from China, the sea shells, and the curios on the whatnot stared back coldly as she looked from the doorway. "What heathen things the men bring home!" she thought.

Her parlor was tight, but she could hear the wind and rain marching by along the road. She closed the door and shook her head. A night like this was hard on the sailors.

She fastened the shawl firmly about her shoulders and pinned up her skirt. With her free hand she protected the light that threatened to go out in the draughts that came down the stairs.

"Sakes alive! What is open?" She hurried to the girls' room, where the wind was coming through the crack under the door. She put down her lamp on the stand in the hall and pushed into the room.

"Well, I never! Just because it's the middle of May you think summer has come!" She shut the window firmly, then glanced at the bed where the two girls were sleeping undisturbed. Eliza's ringlets were making a halo in the dim light from the hall. Adeline was turned away a little. "Thoughtless creatures, sleeping here with a northeast gale blowing and their father and brothers at sea!"

Rain always came in around the chimney when the wind blew from the northward. With Moses Vincent's best skill he could never get the roof tight around it. Mrs. Cleaveland picked up an old rag mat and some worn quilts. She had put a basin there yesterday, but the increasingly high-pitched tone of the drip, drip, drip told her that it was nearly full.

5

The storm was slashing against the window, beating, scratching like some wild thing clawing to get in. Mrs. Cleaveland went over, holding her lamp close, but she could see only her own face mirrored there, distorted by the rain. Suddenly with a small, muffled thud something banged against the glass, crashing against the rain-washed windowpane that had reflected her image, and dropped below.

"What was that?" It must have been a bird attracted by the light she held. Still, it seemed like something more, almost an omen, to be struck at that way.

Back in the kitchen she threw a rain cape over her head, reached cautiously out the east door, and picked up a soft little body, bright-plumaged, foreign.

"Would you believe it?" she asked aloud. "You don't belong here."

She turned the warm, wet bird over curiously. Had it been a robin or a sparrow, or even a crow, she would have warmed it by the fire and tried to bring it back to life.

"From South America, likely!" Opening the door, she threw the bird out into the weather.

2

TEN-THIRTY! The clock on the kitchen shelf had just struck the half hour. Mrs. Henry Cleaveland could rest for a few minutes, so she drew up the cushioned rocker to the window and sat down luxuriously. She had been up since four o'clock and had seen the dawn break faintly gray behind the orchard, separating the clouds to let the sun shine through. It was nice this forenoon—warm and clear and calm after the storm.

Mrs. Cleaveland looked around her kitchen. The lamps lined up on the shelf were full of good sperm oil, and their wicks were trimmed clean. There was wood in the woodbox, for Black John always saw to that. The little cupboard behind the stove was well stocked. On the table there were pans of freshly baked bread turned on their sides, showing the crust, crunchy and sweet. The fragrance of coffee lingered, for as usual she had roasted the green coffee beans before breakfast and pounded them in the mortar before she made the drink. She would have to think of some way to circumvent the neighbors who borrowed the Java coffee that Henry brought from sea and sent in return their burnt bread crumbs, chicory, or whatever it was they used. She'd try to use up a little of it with her good coffee each morning so that it would be gone before the men got home.

"Mercy sakes! I declare I'm hungry. I didn't know it until I smelt that stew cooking."

She got up and went to the buttery for a doughnut and a cup with a little sugar in it. She had left some coffee on the back of the stove.

It was warm, so she opened the east window, and a little breeze came in laden with the scent of apple blossoms and moist earth and the sound of bees humming. The voice of John came to her as he alternately shouted at the horse and cajoled him with high-pitched laughter. John wasn't much of a hand with outdoor things. She stood there looking out. It was quiet and peaceful enough, but in a little while there'd be four more men on the place.

When she finished her coffee, Mrs. Cleaveland rinsed out the cup, then sat down again. She took up the work that lay half-finished in the basket on the shelf by the window. Eliza was hard on her stockings, but she'd have to knit her own. A great girl of fourteen ought to be able to keep herself in stockings. Addie could manage, though she was only twelve. The men would all be coming home, and they would need more socks.

Had they received the box she had sent by Captain

Cottle? she wondered. Her thoughts went back to that fall two years ago when she had heard that the *Ocmulgee* would weigh anchor and set sail from Holmes's Hole on the morning tide. There was no time to lose, so she hastily packed up shirts and socks and underwear, a few glasses of jelly, and a fruitcake soldered into a tin. She and the girls wrote letters. It was wet and cold on the plains road that morning. The box she was carrying grew heavier. Since it wouldn't fit into the saddlebags, she strapped it to the pommel of the saddle, but as the horse jogged the edges hit against his withers. She stuffed her heavy skirt under it; then the corners bit into her leg. The wet, frosty scrub oaks whipped against her ankles. She should have taken the broader road, but it was longer, and she was determined that the ship should not get under way without her bit of cargo.

Very likely the things hadn't reached them after all. You never knew whether these whalers were going to meet or not. One might be cruising around in some new whaling ground when they thought she was in port, but they often found the looked-for vessel or some ship that knew her whereabouts. There were definite whaling grounds where they met, and the men looked pretty sharp for another Vineyard ship. All the boys were brought up together. It wasn't like the New Bedford whalers that recruited their crews from any place they could get them. They had crews made up of Tom, Dick, and Harry—sometimes the scum of the earth. There might be one sailor from home, or there might be two, but usually only the captains knew each other, and sometimes they wished they didn't. Some of them would cut each others' throats if one got more whales than another.

There was that time when Henry, captain of the *Luminary*, was cruising in the Indian Ocean and nearly started a mutiny on the *Huntress* by getting more whales than Captain Sherman. She'd heard Henry tell of the voyage, and there was another record of it in *Voice from the Forecastle of a Whaleship*. Henry was having pretty fair luck, but the *Huntress* was "clean." Two days later they "spoke" again. The *Huntress* was still clean, and when her crew saw the *Luminary* cutting in two more whales they grumbled considerably. They might have just cause, for anybody that complained as much as Sherman did about the amount of food the men ate couldn't have been much of a captain. You can't expect men to work on empty stomachs.

That was the time James sailed on the *Hopewell* as second mate, when he and his father met in the North Pacific. James thought the *Luminary* was in the Indian Ocean, but she'd been around the world, and here she was, gamming with the *Hopewell*.

Mrs. Cleaveland reached for a certain logbook from the long row of cloth-bound volumes on the shelf. *Luminary, Leonidas, Morning Star, Hopewell.* Mrs. Cleaveland knew them as well as she knew the names of her children. She chuckled each time she read that entry in the second mate's neat hand. James always took pains with his logbooks, and Captain Littlefield had given him this one at the end of the voyage.

She turned the pages carefully until she came to the heading August, 1845—the 384th day of the voyage.

384. Sunday, August 24.

Commences with Strong breeze from the North. Ship under double reefe topsailes. At Sunset Spoke the Ship *Luminary* of Warren And Father came on Board and Glad was I to see him. Later saw severall Humpbacks. At 11 A.M. went on Board the *Luminary*. The Lande plaine in Sight. So ends.

Latt. 55:56

Mrs. Cleaveland repeated that sentence, "And Father came on board and Glad was I to see him." After several years away James and his father had met in the North Pacific.

She would have liked to be present at that meeting. Yet she knew that James, as second mate, would have tried to conceal his feelings, to make his dignity equal the captain's. And Henry would have shaken hands firmly and said, "Well, Son!" But James had seen the happiness in his eyes, seen it and returned it. "Glad was I to see him."

She read another entry.

385. Monday, August 25.

Commences with fine weather, the Capt. on Board of the *Luminary*. At three P.M. the Boats from Both Ships Lowered for whales. The mate of the *Luminary* struck one and sunk him. At six P.M. spoke the Ship *Midas* of New Bedford. At 8 P.M. the Capt. came on Board. Latter part a gale from N.N.E. In company with the *Luminary*. So ends this day.

For a month or so they had kept in contact with each other, frequently chasing the same whales, occasionally stopping to gam, being able to see the sails of each other's vessels in the distance. Then the *Luminary*, near the end of her voyage, had sailed on.

"Now where's that other time?" Mrs. Cleaveland said to herself as she thumbed through the pages. "Ah, here."

709. Tuesday, July 7, 1846.

Commences with fine weather. Lowered once for whales at 4 P.M. Spoke the *Metacom* of New Bedford, Capt. Smith. Capt. came on Board and my brother Sylvanus. Latter part saw a whale going Quick. Lowered for him to no purpose.

Yes, that was the place where a man went to see his brothers or his sons or his neighbors—to the Pacific Ocean.

Henry and the two boys had come back, one at a time, had taken Daniel, the little one, and gone off together aboard the *Niantic*. It was nearly four years now since she had seen any of them—and all this Gold Rush had come up since. Her men had been right in the thick of things. In fact, the *Niantic* had been one of the first ships to take a load of passengers from Panama, for Henry had been at Valparaíso when word was brought of activity in California. Henry had refitted his ship and with his three sons and the rest of the crew had sailed for Panama to gather up the crowd of gold seekers waiting there and take them to San Francisco.

They had been forced to abandon the *Niantic*, for the men had all rushed off to the gold fields. They'd bought the smaller *Mary Wilder* then and made trips to China, bringing back goods to trade in the fast-growing

JAMES FREEMAN CLEAVELAND
DANIEL ATHEARN CLEAVELAND
SYLVANUS CLEAVELAND

One of the CLEAVELAND *ships, painted in China by a Chinese artist*

city. James was now captain of her and Daniel, first mate. Daniel had been only eighteen when he left. She supposed he would never have a ship of his own. He had something else in mind. If this voyage were profitable he planned to study medicine. She didn't know where he took that from. He'd never been quite as virile as the other sons. Sylvanus and James, she knew, would always follow the sea.

Her thoughts were interrupted by a shuffle of feet outside. "Mercy sakes! Who is that coming in at this time of day?" she said to herself. "Come right in," she called without rising.

The door opened slowly, and Richard Thompson's head appeared, followed gradually by his body and brought up by his short, sturdy legs.

"Good morning, Richard. Come right in and sit down."

"What's the news from abroad, Mis' Cleaveland?"

"You asking me for news, when all I've done is to sit here looking out of the window? I thought maybe you had some good news for me—or a letter."

"You never know when you see a letter whether it's good news or whether it ain't."

"Well, you know the one that wrote it was still alive when 'twas written."

"That ain't sayin' much these days," he drawled, "with folks gallivantin' around the globe so it takes three-four months before you can hear from 'em, and two-three years before you can see 'em."

"That's nothing new to me, Richard," Mrs. Cleaveland said with pride. "It's been my lot and portion to have menfolks at sea ever since I can remember. . . . What are you padding through your pockets for, Richard?"

"I was a searchin' for somethin'. . . . " After a pause he continued, "The Athearns wa'n't much at seafarin'. They had sense enough to stay at home. At least the ones your folks come from. There's Squire George. After he'd been off island to Harvard College he'd no notion of heavin' his eddication overboard."

"No, my grandfather never took to the sea. But all Henry's people were sea captains."

"How *was* the cap'n, last you heard?"

"Very well, I thank you."

"And the boys?"

"Yes, all well."

"You kinda put all your eggs in one basket, lettin' 'em all go off together aboard the same ship."

"You might say so, but let me tell you, 'twas a pretty good basket to put 'em in, as long as Henry Cleaveland's arm was through the handle."

"Ships is oncertan, kinda."

"Not so uncertain to a sailor, Richard, as the land is."

"When do you look for James, Mis' Cleaveland?"

"I hardly expect him before next month."

"Pretty smart, him bein' cap'n!"

"They say the *Mary Wilder* is a nice little vessel, though she's not so large as the *Niantic*," Mrs. Cleaveland conceded.

Richard edged around to get a good look at Mrs. Cleaveland's expression before he asked slyly, "What about this woman of James's?"

"Saphrony Cathcart? I hope James has had sense

enough to write her a letter." To herself she added, "Trouble enough I had getting that match under way without writing his love letters for him."

"Well, I dunno about her, but they's a letter for *you* from the Pacific."

"A letter? You don't say! Where is it?" she asked eagerly.

"Here in my pocket. I couldn't find it at first, so I thought I'd keep on a-talkin'."

"You might have brought along your fiddle and played it."

Richard ignored her slighting allusion to his music. "They say James is on his way home."

"Yes, I thought likely."

"Cap'n Jernegan give him a cargo of oil to freight."

"You keep on a talkin', Richard, and I won't have to open my letter to find out the news."

"Go right ahead, Mis' Cleaveland. Open it up. Don't mind me. Fact is, I'd like to hear what he says."

In frigid tones Mrs. Cleaveland replied, "There's plenty of time. It isn't likely I shall get another letter right away. I guess this one will keep as long as I have company."

Richard shuffled about a bit, curious and eager, but Mrs. Cleaveland's hands were folded serenely in her lap. He knew by the looks of her back that it would be useless for him to wait any longer. "Guess I might as well be movin' on," he said.

He sidled out, but as he went he turned with a kind of chortle. "I *should* like to hear more about what's goin' on."

"Now what's Richard Thompson got up his sleeve?" Alert, she rose. Before Richard closed the door, she called bitingly, "If you know more than I do for once in your life, I don't think strange you're so pleased."

A trifle sobered, Richard headed off down the lane toward home.

3

M_{RS.} C_{LEAVELAND} was standing now, every nerve taut, a tall, dignified woman of forty-six. She was looking after Richard as he waddled down the road toward his house. Tense as she was, she commented on his walk, with the short stubby legs trying to catch up with one another. Green-looking fellow he was! He'd never been to sea like the other boys.

She turned the letter over in her hand, thoughtfully. Yes, it was James's writing. She turned back to the window. Richard was still in sight, walking his comedy slouch. Now what's in this letter that he knows about and thinks is so funny? Who else would have letters from the Pacific? Somebody aboard some whaler might have written to Caroline. She'd have no better sense than to read it to Richard. He wouldn't act so queer if the *Mary Wilder* were lost or anybody injured. Richard might like to see them come down a peg, but he was never mali-

17

cious. Some member of her family, she concluded, had made a fool of himself.

She sat down to think, turning the letter over meanwhile in her lap. "You don't suppose," she thought, "they've gone and invested all their money in some wildcat gold mine! They say this gold fever on the West Coast is catching. All the young men in the place that never left home before are traipsing out there as fast as they can." There were David Mayhew and Brandon, real likely young fellows, walking down to Holmes's Hole to take the ship, telling how when they came back they'd buy a horse and carriage and ride like a sea captain. There's a place they call Camp Vineyard. Most likely everyone in it homesick. Then they trickle back, still poor and sick besides. No, nothing but whaling would ever get Henry. He was as levelheaded a husband as a woman could wish for. He had been a good many voyages, too.

She knew it wasn't James, her eldest son, captain now. Sylvanus might get himself into some kind of a scrape, but he could always get himself out again. It must be Daniel. Daniel never wanted to go to sea, anyhow. He went just as a matter of course. Everybody did that was any account. It was part of their schooling.

Well, now, what had Daniel done? He hadn't got drunk. Her boys never took anything. Henry wouldn't have a drop on board, except for medicine. Was some woman at the bottom of this? She might have thought of that before. Handsome men like hers had to watch sharp for such pitfalls. Yes, sir! That would be just the sort of thing that would be pleasing to Richard Thompson. He'd like to see me with something to be a mite ashamed of.

"I shouldn't be ashamed." She tossed her head proudly. "It wouldn't be Daniel's fault but the fault of the huzzy that got hold of him."

She picked up the letter and opened it.

There were two pages, closely written in James's clear, firm hand, dated Honolulu, November 29, 1851. He told all the happenings of the last few months, of the ships from home that were stopping there at the Sandwich Islands, of the weather, of whales, of his ship. He'd taken a cargo of oil from the ship *Jeanette* and also 600 barrels from the *William Thompson*. The *Mary Wilder* was pretty well loaded now, and he should leave in a few weeks. She might even make port before this letter reached his mother. And when he came he'd have his wife. . . .

Her eyes quickly scanned the rest of the letter. Her mouth shut in grim, firm lines with the corners drawn down. She rose deliberately, opened the lid of the shining new stove and put the letter in.

She went back to the rocking chair, heavily, slowly. Keen and witty before, she seemed to become dull and blank and listless—but within her a fire of passion was raging. Jealousy, anger, hatred were pricking her with ugly jabs, although her face remained calm. She sat there, rocking, rocking.

The clock on the shelf ticked, ticked, ticked, ticked.

An oriole sang in the orchard—a sharp metallic song.

A truck wagon went by, empty, rattling.

A rooster crowed.

The chair rocked rhythmically.

The girls came home from school with cheeks and eyes bright.

"They say there's a ship in from the Pacific, Mother. Did we get a letter?"

"Yes."

"May we read it?"

"No."

"What's happened? Is Father—all right?"

"*He's* all right."

"The boys? Are the ships lost?"

"No."

Eliza looked at Adeline and saw that her eyes were misty and her mouth quivering. She went to the stove where the stew was simmering and took a spoonful for Addie and some for herself. There were no dumplings, so Eliza cut off big slices of the new bread and spread things out on the red and white cloth.

The girls tried to eat, but they could not swallow, for the atmosphere felt hostile. Their mother still sat by the window, rocking. They pushed aside their plates in silence, then tiptoed out. Even school was preferable.

If they only knew what the trouble was! They longed to stop at Caroline Luce's to find out the news, but their pride held them. If they had some money they could go to Rotch's store for a licorice stick or some horehound. John D. Rotch always knew what was going on. But their pockets were empty.

Eliza left Adeline at the little school by the Mill Pond, and went on her way to the Academy. The girls were gathered in knots which separated as she came in, but from one group she overheard a heated discussion.

"He married her in the Sandwich Islands? She must be black," one girl inferred.

"No, they aren't black in the Sandwich Islands."

"Well, dark brown, with kinky hair—almost as bad."

"Nobody said she was an islander. She might be a missionary."

"But I thought he was going to marry Saphrony Cath . . . " The speaker saw Eliza standing there and left the word unfinished.

Eliza turned, went to the cloakroom, and buried her face in her little jacket. Now she could see it all. That was the matter with Mother! That was what the letter had said! James had married somebody "from off."

4

IT WAS some time before Mary Ann Cleaveland showed any of her accustomed interest in affairs. John had come in, seen her sitting there, scratched his woolly head, then dished out stew and set it before her. He made a cup of tea for her, took his own, and left.

Mrs. Cleaveland ate mechanically.

And then, unexpectedly, a smile raised the corners of her lips. She went back over the years. Into her thoughts came snatches of the past—bitter things and hard things, the sweet and the precious. Life lay revealed, each episode intense from her keen suffering.

Yes, James had always carried out his own ideas. She had tried to guide him. She had tried to force him. But he had gone his own way.

Her body still ached at the remembrance of the time he had beaten her, but her eyes twinkled. He had been climbing out at night, by means of the grapevine over the east door. He wanted to be out under the stars, to feel the dewy grass under his feet, and against his ankles the little fronds of redtop. He wanted to hear the night noises, the new lambs bleating and their mothers' calls, the sleepy sounds the nesting birds make, and the long-drawn-out repetition of the whippoorwill. He wanted to look at the stars, to see the Great Dipper standing out bright in the northern sky, and the Milky Way making a halo for the earth. And he wanted to share these things with his little brothers.

Now when Mary Ann Cleaveland put her children to bed for the night, she expected them to stay there. There was to be no gallivanting around in their night clothes. They might get their deaths of cold mooning around out there in the orchard. She had long suspected this, though she had thought James, at any rate, was old enough to know better. Now she had caught them red-handed. She saw them climb out stealthily, Sylvanus and Daniel following James down the arbor.

"I'll put a stop to this," she said.

So she took a sheet from the linen closet, ran around through the orchard, and hid behind the trunk of the largest apple tree, near the path.

She had not long to wait. The three boys were coming along, hand in hand. They were talking in whispers, awed by the silence about them.

"First thing—" James was beginning to find his voice. "First thing you do is to find the North Star. You won't ever get lost if you know where the North Star is and keep watch of it."

She laughed to herself at his earnestness, at the eager

listeners who would so soon scamper back to their beds.

"You want to find the Dipper," James continued, standing still and pointing it out to them.

"I see it, James."

"Then follow those two stars. Not the handle, Dan'l, the place where you drink from. Come over here a ways. You can see it better."

They were walking along near the fence now. She mustn't wait too long. She put the sheet over her, quickly, silently, and, gliding noiselessly from behind the big tree, danced dreamily before them; then suddenly she turned.

The effect on the children was all she had hoped for. The two youngest cowered close to their bigger brother. She couldn't see their eyes, but she knew they were big and round. James's thick hair was probably standing straight and crisp like a cat's. He stood stock-still in his tracks.

A moment of astonishment! Then he spoke firmly to the boys. "Come, get along over that fence and stay there." He shoved them when they tripped over their long nightshirts. The mock ghost fluttered and hovered near.

With the younger children safe, he turned like a flash, grasped her by the flowing garments, struck out at her head with his fists, kicked and punched and pounded. "I've got you, you old devil!" he shouted. Seeing victory on their side, Sylvanus and Daniel stood up on the fence and cheered.

She was forced to cry for mercy. "James, James, it's your mother." Then he let go.

2 4

"What you doing, Ma, out here in the night air?" he said.

Her quick mind darted to Honolulu, where James was married. She saw the *Mary Wilder* with James and his wife on board. "Some stranger's got him," she muttered.

A nice little lad, he was! Her first! She could remember just how he looked in her arms as she sat by the big fireplace over at Grandfather George Athearn's. She was seventeen when she had brought her first baby over to show him to "Squire George." He had kicked and crowed like all babies, but she had thought he was different. He was, too. He was strong and sturdy and showed a mind of his own even then. He had played with the buttons on Squire George's red vest, which he still wore on Sundays. It was old then and had lost some of its grandeur since the time he had sat for his portrait.

James liked to go there—to Squire George's. Even when Aunt Becky reigned supreme and used to haze him so, he would sit in the big wing chair in the fireplace and try to make himself small, so she wouldn't see him. But Aunt Becky always did. She would come along and push the wood over from one side to the other, then say, "James, get up, that's a good boy, and shift this wood back into place." Funny, some people never could let a man rest. She herself liked to see the menfolks comfortable. They had their work to do. When they come home let them sit down.

Well, James had gone and got somebody to wait on him now. Let her do it, too!

How she used to look forward to Saturdays, when

James would come home from school. She'd sent him to the shire town to get the best there was in education. He'd be tired from walking so far—nearly nine miles, it was, from Edgartown. But he'd never give in. He used to stop at Wintucket, and an old woman who lived there would give him apple pie and milk. Old people always liked James.

James had been quite a hand with the girls, too. She didn't think he'd have taken to foreigners, though. What shenanigans do you suppose that girl went through to get him! The girls in the village used to be good enough for him. He'd had good times here. Before he ever went to sea (he couldn't have been more than fifteen), she had bought him a beautiful new coat with a long broadcloth cape. He came to her and asked if she couldn't make holes in the cape. "Can't you slit out the seams here and here?"

"What do you want holes in it for, I'd like to know?" she asked.

"So the girls can take my arm coming home from parties."

She hadn't bothered with the holes. It's a wonder, though, he hadn't cut off the cape, the headstrong critter.

It was time he married, to be sure, but there was Saphrony Cathcart. A nice girl! He ought to have married her. They'd known each other all their lives. She had asked her to supper and had given James a ring to give her. Only last Sunday at meeting, she'd seen 'Phrony wearing it, turning it round on her finger and studying it kind of thoughtful. A plain girl she was, but a good cook and a "faculized" seamstress. Why, good land, she made all the millinery in the village. Yes, a good steady girl.

Too bad she was so homely! Still she wouldn't be as likely to cut up any didos while her husband was away at sea. You had to think of those things with the men gone a Cape Horn voyage.

But a foreigner! You never could tell what they'd do. Never could depend on them to do except what was unlikely. There was Captain Leroy with that Frenchwoman. Nobody could understand her, even when she spoke English. She'd thought James would know better than to get wed to some fly-by-night.

Now that he *was* married, what was he going to do with the woman? *She* didn't want her in the house. "The huzzy! I'd like to tear her eyes out!"

Somewhat startled at her own violence, she hesitated. But the interval brought back pictures of James, her first son, her comrade, her mainstay. "Yes, I should. I'd like to tear her eyes out. And when she gets here, I'll show her how to act!"

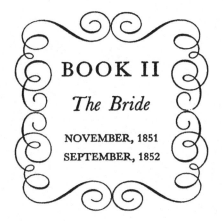

BOOK II

The Bride

NOVEMBER, 1851
SEPTEMBER, 1852

5

ONLY the vast blue ocean in sight, and Mary Carlin had gazed at it for weeks from the deck of the *Emma Prescott*. One day after another, each like the one preceding—no violent storms, no sudden calms, just the steady push of the trade winds. The sails were neatly filled, the brig pulsing along, dipping in the waves, bobbing up again, dipping and bobbing and pulsing with the wind.

Mary hated it. A storm would be better, something definitely disturbing, rather than this continued unsettled feeling in her stomach. She couldn't lie down except when necessity forced her to, for her cabin was a poor place, the air foul with pent-up odors from the galley.

There had been a stop at Tahiti, but Mary had not been permitted to go ashore, and the women who came out to the vessel had made her ashamed for her sex. Even the poor natives of New South Wales had covered themselves up with blankets when they approached the city.

31

What would Mother have thought! Mother had been so particular about modesty in her girls, even with six children.

The thought of her mother filled Mary with longing. In her eager young ignorance she had looked forward to this voyage. She hadn't thought it would last so long and be so dull and take her so far away. She'd never get up courage for the long trip back. She began to be afraid she might never see her home again.

Mary closed her eyes and pictured the little house she had left, clothing its shabby boards in a patina of weathered softness. The scraggly vines had flowered, the dirty street in the new city of Sydney, Australia, became a pleasant road—and Father, coming home from his day's work with his carpenter's chest slung over his shoulder, was smiling and joking merrily and kissing them with good clean breath, as in his better days. Mother was the same as ever, calm and dignified and ladylike, ready to stretch out her hand to touch Mary's forehead. If only Mother could stroke her hair now, she wouldn't feel so miserably sick!

"Why did she send me away?"

"I beg your pardon?"

"Oh, I didn't know you were there, Mr. Lohn. I must have been talking aloud when I thought I was just thinking."

"You aren't sorry you came, are you, little girl?"

"Mr. Lohn, I'm sixteen." Mary spoke with a queer combination of dignity and archness.

"I'm sorry, Miss Carlin, if I presumed, but really you looked quite small and discouraged."

"I'm not at all." Mary sat up straight. Her cheeks were bright, and she was determined to "behave like a lady" as Mother had advised. She spoke up quickly, lest Mr. Lohn go away. "Tell me more about Ellen."

"All right. Where shall I start?"

"At the very beginning, where Ellen and John pitched the little camp on the bank of the river and built a sluiceway, and Ellen cooked for the men, and John found gold. I've never heard half enough about it.

"There don't seem to be many details. John found gold. That's the important thing. Many of them didn't. Some found it and couldn't keep it."

"But John had Ellen there with him!"

"By George, you're right. I thought it was luck, but probably it was Ellen. When she thought they had enough John set up business in San Francisco and they built a fine house. That's where you are going now."

"And they have a piano."

"Yes, a beautiful one, inlaid with mother-of-pearl, with a tone like a bell."

"And I'm to have music lessons."

"Yes, and dancing, too, most likely. You'll meet all the gay young blades of Frisco—and won't the belles be jealous of those dark curls and Irish eyes."

Mary blushed. She had forgotten the dull ache of homesickness. The future looked bright once more. She hummed a little tune—then suddenly broke off. "It was fortunate you came to Sydney."

"Yes?"

"Mother would never have allowed me to come so far alone."

"It wouldn't have been wise."

"And then your knowing Ellen! It seemed to bring her close. I didn't seem to be going so far away, going with you and Mrs. Lohn."

At the mention of his wife Mr. Lohn started. He had left her for a full half hour. She was lying in her cabin with a wet towel on her head, as she had lain most of the voyage, her nose pinched up and her lips a thin bluish line. Why didn't she come out on deck like this plucky little girl and forget her troubles by talking to Mary? He rose quickly. He'd go and get her. Lord! A half hour! There'd be hell to pay. But he'd tell her. He'd tell her to come up and learn some spunk from that child.

Henry Lohn wouldn't have been so rash if he had realized that Mary Carlin's blue eyes and dark curls, her full red lips and round cheeks—and her voice, vibrant and young, were as largely responsible as the ocean for his wife's attacks of migraine.

"Excuse me," he said, and went quickly below.

Mary looked out at the sea. It stretched ahead in an unbroken expanse. It extended as far as she could see on either side. In back, nothing but the wake that curled away from the vessel and finally lost itself in the distance. And underneath there was the throb of it, steady, steady, dip and lift, dip and lift. "Oh, dear God, how much longer?"

6

THE beauty of early morning shimmered like some tangible thing—like a colored veil of sheerest net thrown over the world. The *Emma Prescott* with her sails set was like a bird—a wild white swan, half swimming, half flying past fairy islands. After nine weeks of sailing over the Pacific Ocean they had reached the Sandwich Islands.

Mary stood up in the bow with the sailor on watch. At dawn she had seen the lava-streaked crater of Mauna Loa against the sky. She had seen thin threads of smoke rising from some distant native village. Now she could distinguish grass huts and palm-thatched roofs. She could hear the even roll of water as it touched white beaches. She breathed island-scented air.

They were getting closer. Soon they would land at Honolulu. Mary'd be able to run along the streets. No, she must remember—"always be a lady!" Well, she could walk. She'd be on land. She'd be free from the close, cramped quarters of shipboard.

They were entering the harbor. The sails were being lowered until the *Emma Prescott* looked like the other ships —whalers and traders, packed side by side along the waterfront, with their rigging like winter trees towering into the sky—as high almost as the palms that waved their great bouquet tops above the houses.

The other passengers, Mr. Lohn, Mr. Moan, Mr. Cushing, and even Mrs. Lohn had come on deck. They stayed aft, but Mary stood in the bow. She began to sing. No one on deck could hear her above the thunder of the sails as they descended, above the commands of Captain Fligg and the shouts of the boatswain. Her song went out toward the land, toward the green hills and trees, toward the red earth and the houses in which people lived, to the little town nestled down between the mountains and the sea, to the men standing on the wharves, commenting critically on the maneuvering of the vessel.

Mary noticed a group of several men standing a little apart, one of them a tall, broad-shouldered man, stately and clean-cut. She couldn't hear what they were saying, but they were obviously talking about the *Emma Prescott*, their glass leveled at her bow.

Mary sang on, watching all the while how the vessel came nearer to land, how crowds of natives with ropes, walking along a sort of bar, towed the vessel to her berth. She watched the houses in the village assume individuality. She read the sign "Custom House." The belfry of the chapel stood out. She kept on singing.

"That dreadful child!" muttered Mrs. Lohn.

HONOLULU HARBOR *as it looked when the Cleavelands were married in the Seamen's Bethel, which can be seen at the extreme left*

HONOLULU *from old light house—about* 1859

(Photographs, courtesy of Williams Studio, Honolulu)

"Shall I go and call her aft?"

"No, no, Henry," Mrs. Lohn interposed quickly. "Let her be. Another month and we'll be shut of her—I hope." She added the last two words quietly and a little doubtfully. Henry was very attractive, if she did say it who shouldn't.

"Nonsense, my dear. She's been no trouble at all. I'd like to see more of her in San Francisco, to see how she develops."

"She'll develop into a huzzy, and she won't have far to go—making a show of herself standing there, singing!"

But Mary stopped suddenly. Two young men on the wharf were waving to her. She was about to return their friendly greeting when she remembered her mother's words, "Always be a lady." So she merely smiled and moved aft towards the group of passengers who noticed, with various emotions, that the bright color in Mary's cheeks was very becoming.

7

A FEW weeks ago Mary would not have believed it possible to enjoy a meal aboard the *Emma Prescott*. But she was looking forward to this evening. Captain Fligg was celebrating and was at the same time returning some favor done him by another captain in port. This was to be a fine dinner with fresh food from the island, the ship lying quiet at her berth.

Mary looked anxiously at her wardrobe. There would be no difficulty in choosing what to wear, but how could she make that dark silk dress look a little festive—the one that Cecily had worn? She had no lace mantle, no ribbons.

"I have it. I'll cut the lace ruffle from my best petticoat to make a fichu."

Flushed from her haste with scissors and needle, Mary entered the small drawing room and found the company already assembled. Mrs. Lohn, tight-lipped, was seated uncomfortably on the edge of a chair. The men were all standing, Mr. Lohn with his hand on his wife's shoulder.

Captain Fligg was strutting around, showing the strangers certain details of his vessel, opening up space-saving cabinets hidden in the paneling.

He bustled forward when he saw Mary. "Miss Carlin, I'd like to make you acquainted with Captain Cleaveland of the *Mary Wilder*, and his brother, first mate of the same vessel."

The two young men bowed low, and as they straightened Mary recognized them as the two she had noticed standing on the wharf as the *Emma Prescott* entered the harbor.

She smiled her recognition, and the younger brother grinned disarmingly. Captain Cleaveland had meant to make no secret of the fact that he sought her company, but it was as though he was seeing her for the first time. He had watched her trim figure from the shore, he had heard her singing, but now he was looking into her eyes. He was conscious of her bosom rising and falling beneath the white fichu, with the hibiscus flower tucked into its folds in place of a brooch. He had never met a girl like her with life and dignity at the same time. Usually girls with high spirits were silly, and sedate girls were a bore. He liked them all—but this one! He'd never seen a girl like her before.

And Mary, looking up with laughter in her eyes because these young men had perhaps sought her company, found Captain James Cleaveland looking seriously at her. Her mood changed in response. She recognized sooner than he, for all his experience, that there was something vibrant in the air between them—that if she were to touch his hand . . .

39

"Do you sing?" Mr. Cleaveland, the younger man, asked innocently from one side.

The spell was broken. Mary looked up coquettishly at Mr. Cleaveland, first mate of the *Mary Wilder*. He knew very well she could sing.

The cabin boy spoke to Captain Fligg. Then, quietly summoning the guests, the captain, with Mrs. Lohn, led the way to their places at the table.

Ah! Hawaiian fish, wine, good red beef and Yorkshire pudding, sweet potatoes, and vegetables and fruits that Mary had never before tasted and had only seen in her stolen visits to the waterfront of Sydney.

Mary, half-starved with the long diet of potatoes and corned beef, which had grown saltier and saltier as the voyage lengthened, could hardly wait to sit down, but, surprisingly, she could eat only a little. It was as though new emotions were taking up all the space in her being. But Captain Cleaveland ate well.

Captain Fligg told stories of experiences in various islands in the Pacific—escapes from cannibals, wrecks on unfriendly shores—and Captain Cleaveland told stories, too. He told of Saint Elmo's fire that lighted up the masts of his ship one night when he came from the Japan Sea. He told of rescuing the crew of a French whaler in the Okhotsk. He seemed to be talking entirely to Captain Fligg.

The man on the other side was ready to talk to Mary. He was almost as young as she. At least he wasn't much more than twenty. "Have you been at sea long?" she asked him.

"I left home for the first time about four years ago." He told her he'd been homesick at first. He didn't like the sea. He wanted to be a doctor. But where he came from every man that amounted to anything sailed a voyage or two, so of course he went to sea. "I got so's I could about stand on my feet and that was all, when the captain headed towards home with a good cargo of oil. But when we got to Valparaíso Father heard of the Gold Rush, and nothing must do but he ship his oil home by the *Carrie Fowler* that was pretty near clean and go up to Panama for a load of passengers and take 'em to Frisco."

Now everyone was listening to Daniel Cleaveland. Panama! San Francisco! The Gold Rush! He gave his older brother a triumphant look.

But Captain Fligg was entertaining another captain. No first mate could be allowed to monopolize the conversation. He looked across to the other end of the table. "Have you just come from Frisco, Cap'n Cleaveland?"

"I've been there off and on for two years, Cap'n, and I'll be glad to get back home." And he told of the first days in the city, of entering the Golden Gate with his father as master of the ship, of steering up into the bay, past green islands, then taking one of the boats up the river with a mess of crazy passengers aboard that would jump off whenever they thought progress was slow— never to be seen again. "They'd died from starvation, most likely, or been murdered for the bit of flour and prospecting tools they had about them. Good men turned to thieves and rascals and murderers."

Mary listened. She thought of her sister Ellen with her husband John McCloskey. "They had to go through this!" she thought. "After the voyage across the ocean."

She listened. Now Captain Cleaveland was talking to *her*. He wanted to interest her. Here were these other people, Mr. and Mrs. Lohn and Captain Fligg, yet he was talking to her, Mary Carlin. Never before had she been so singled out from among older people.

"Yes, we've been over to Japan and China, too, and got some goods to sell in Frisco."

Young Mr. Cleaveland interposed with a few quiet words to Mary.

The captain went on. "They'd buy anything. The way they put up buildings was a disgrace. So sham-built they'd tumble down if you looked at 'em. And packed in so close they'd catch afire if you lit a match."

"That's right," Mr. Lohn agreed.

"One time when we came from Japan we saw the light of the whole city, pretty near, going up in smoke."

Mary was startled. Was her sister all right?

The captain reassured her. This was over a year ago. They built right up again. "We could see the warehouse where our goods were stowed standing out against the flames."

"We thought 'twas a goner for sure," the mate said to Mary.

But his brother's voice rose above his. "Twas pretty near the only thing in that section that withstood the heat. *That right, Mr. Cleaveland?*" The question was delivered in the captain's quarter-deck tone. The young mate, startled, was about to stand smartly and say, "Aye, aye, sir." But he caught himself. He realized that his brother, the captain, was merely serving notice that this was *his* girl. He'd brook no interference.

4 2

"That's right," he said humbly.

Mary looked at him, young like herself and homesick. She looked back at the captain—a powerful man with clean-cut features, dark beard, and eyes that danced with a devil-may-care light, glowed with calm assurance, or twinkled with humor that came to his mind ahead of his lips and lighted up his face from within.

She looked around the table at the faces all watching the captain, listening to his stories, to his tales of adventure and of the hard early days of California. Her eyes stopped at Mrs. Lohn. Unexpectedly the woman looked quite calm. The tales of shore-front battles, fire and water, and inadequate housing were not troubling her at all. For the first time since she had seen Mary, Mrs. Lohn answered her puzzled look with a smile.

Then Mrs. Lohn turned, still smiling, as Captain Cleaveland spoke to her.

"I'd be pleased, ma'am, if you ladies would join us on a cruise to the Pali tomorrow."

And Mrs. Lohn, looking at Mary, answered graciously, "We'd be charmed, I'm sure, Captain Cleaveland."

Everything, everybody is so nice tonight, thought Mary.

8

A CRUISE to the Pali! Mary didn't know what it was, where, or how they'd go. She didn't know whether they took the little sailing vessel that she had seen coming and going in the harbor, or what kind of ship, but she was eager for the adventure. To her surprise and relief, she found they were to drive part way, at least, and then walk. It seemed any sort of short trip on land or sea was a "cruise" to the captain.

There were duties that kept Captain Fligg in the town, and Captain Cleaveland had ordered his mate to take charge of the *Mary Wilder*, so there were four in the party, Mr. and Mrs. Lohn, Captain Cleaveland, and Mary.

The captain called for them early. A man would come with the horses. He'd left word at the livery stable.

"Can't we walk to the stables?" asked Mary.

"Oh, la, la, to be sure," said Mrs. Lohn, opening her sunshade. But in an aside to Mary, "They kind of like to do things for you, dearie."

44

Captain Cleaveland took Mary's arm and strode along beside her, talking. "We'll have to be careful not to whip them up. There's a law against fast driving."

"There is?"

"Only on Saturdays is the law overlooked, and then, I can tell you, there's some swift horseback riding!"

"Well!"

"Every Saturday afternoon they devote to feats of horsemanship. It's a wonderful sight to see the natives flash by. The women ride as fast as the men. A handsome sight, too! You'll see on Saturday."

"I hope we'll be here then. I don't know how long Captain Fligg means to stop."

"He'll be here at least a week. I made sure of that."

A week, perhaps more, of respite from the sea! And Heaven here in Honolulu!

The horses were eager to be off. Captain Cleaveland and Mr. Lohn helped the ladies into the carriage while the horses' heads were held by a scarred-looking old salt who talked respectfully to the captain.

Then they started off, holding the horses down to a slow trot in the city and driving still more slowly through the lovely countryside. They went through the Nuuanu Valley, past the houses of foreign residents built on the hillside, past native huts. They passed small artificial canals that the natives had dug to water their taro beds. On they went for perhaps six or seven miles, climbing steadily now.

Everywhere there were signs of clever cultivation, but many of the fields had not been harvested.

"What's the matter with them here?" Mr. Lohn asked.

4 5

"They've produced too much. There used to be more of a demand when the whalers stopped here between seasons so thick you couldn't get a berth along the waterfront."

"Where are they now?"

"California."

"Wouldn't you think they could use the surplus there?"

"To be sure they could use it there. Fewer folks would go hungry or pay exhorbitant prices. But there's no way of getting it there. The *Emma Prescott* was pretty well stowed when she made port here. I shipped freight last voyage I took and got good prices for it, too. But I don't want to go into that business. I'm a whaler. And they'll give good prices for sperm oil, too, in that fast-living city."

The road became steeper. There was a small plantation a little further beyond. They'd leave the horses there and proceed on foot.

Mrs. Lohn preferred to walk slowly. "You young folks go on ahead."

Mary had not believed Mrs. Lohn could be so friendly and interesting and kind. 'Twas the sea, thought Mary, excusing her previous ill nature.

Mary and the captain went on, climbing up the rough path. They heard cascades singing among the rocks, and waterfalls tumbling from perpendicular cliffs, falling into pebbly basins.

"Listen," Mary held up her hand. "Wood nymphs playing!" She laughed softly. It was like the echo of the water.

"Maybe you're a nymph. When you laugh it's like a

4 6

waterfall in the forest or like the little brook at home." A trace of longing came into his voice.

Mary looked at him with renewed interest. "You're homesick, too!"

"Hm! Sometimes I just can't hardly stand it I want a good piece of punkin pie so bad. And I want to see the folks at home, and see Ma, and hear her saying funny things. And smell the apple orchard. November's no time for all these green things."

"Things are green in Sydney, now. And some of the trees are flowering."

"Now's Thanksgiving at home, with a little flurry of snow, maybe, and the oak leaves all brown and rustling with the wind. And cornhuskings and quilting parties where you bring the girls home through the woods—and they're scared of skunks or foxes . . . "

Mary clutched his sleeve. "Oh! I think I see a snake!"

"Say, you're a quick little vixen!"

She turned and ran ahead of him, laughing.

With long strides he could hardly catch up. "Be careful!" he called, so she waited.

The road became narrower, rougher. It led the way past a rocky ledge, then suddenly the trail stopped, and they found themselves on the edge of a precipice that dropped sheer into the plain below.

Mary didn't want to stay there. The wind howled through the defile and snatched at her. But Captain Cleaveland was there to keep her from falling.

"The natives used to bring their captives here in ancient times, and they'd plunge below of their own accord," he told her.

4 7

She reached for his hand, and he held hers. He put his arm around her waist. She couldn't fall. She didn't feel dizzy any more. Instead of the wind beating against her, she felt the warmth of this big man's nearness.

"Mary, Mary," he whispered.

She looked up at him, startled. She felt his presence against her like the throb of the sea. Why, he smelt like the sea! His coat even in the sunshine of Hawaii still bore the odor of tar and hemp and salt spray. She could see him before a wheel, facing into a gale, with the wind—a wild wind like this one—pitching the ship and shaking the sails, rolling the cargo and righting it again. His arms were around her; his eyes were looking into hers; his lips were close. She could feel the lift of the ocean, dip and lift, dip and lift. She no longer feared it—with James.

9

THROUGHOUT the next week Mary was troubled with misgivings. Her mother had started her out for San Francisco, had sacrificed to send her, had given up the company of her youngest daughter—the baby whom she loved most of all.

And in San Francisco wonderful things awaited her. Ellen, alone in a strange country, needed one of her own people. She would do everything in her power to make Mary happy. She owned a fine house, she could give Mary every opportunity—theaters, parties, good clothes, dancing and music.

These tales of San Francisco that she had recently heard had stirred Mary strangely. The city reminded her of Sydney, new and growing from small beginnings into a mighty power, with the bustle and commotion and enthusiasm of its crowd of adventurous inhabitants. She knew the activity of a busy port and loved it.

But in Sydney she had been on the outer edge, the

daughter of a poor carpenter. She could go to the grand balls at which the governor presided, but she must sit in a back seat watching other people dance, envying them their long silk gowns, their high coiffures, their laces and ribbons, and sweet, elegant manners. She would go with her brothers, but she was never boisterous as they were. She'd sit quietly watching the polka until she knew it by heart, and she'd try to act, as Mother always told her, "like a little lady."

But now a vision appeared of herself in a fashionable gown of blue-gray like her eyes, with its long folds of silk rustling about her ankles, with her dark curls twisted around her finger until they lay in rolls along the nape of her neck and bobbed when she bowed to the other ladies. And she'd step before the crowd up to the piano, bow again, move her fan gently, and sing, sing to the whole assembly.

On the other hand this sea captain would take her far away into the unknown, where everything was strange, everything except the ocean.

And yet when she saw James striding along to join her, when she heard his voice, hearty and jolly, when she felt his hand grasp hers and his eyes look down at her tenderly, then she'd go to the ends of the earth with him —over the ocean.

The power to choose her course seemed out of her hands. She was drifting, drawn by a current of emotion towards this man and his way of life, which might open up a new vista or might mean relinquishing all she held most dear. It was not for her to decide. Fate had chosen for her.

50

Had they been left alone, James and Mary might have drifted apart even after that moment on the heights of Pali. For Mary was on her way to San Francisco. She didn't want her course diverted. And James was a man of sound judgment, brought up to look squarely at practical facts. He knew very little of Mary. She was so different from the girls he had courted! Yet that, he realized, was part of her charm. She was full of life and yet so serious and quiet at times, like a deep stream with pools and eddies and green banks. Her laughter was not the ripple of shallows but the ruffle of the wind against the current. He knew that her strangeness might not sit well at home. And besides, he'd left Saphrony Cathcart there. She was the first girl his mother had ever been able to countenance. 'Phrony knew the same folks, went to the same church—Godfrey! This girl was a Roman Catholic! A little Irish emigrant from Sydney!

Yet her voice was like music, her diction clearer than his own, except for that Irish talk, and he liked that. She hadn't been at school as much as his New England sisters, Mary had admitted, but her mother had taught her at home. Her mother! She spoke often of her mother. There was good stuff there somewhere. Still, she was a foreigner—you couldn't get away from that fact—and he'd better keep away from her.

Well, he had to see Captain Fligg on a small matter of business. He'd like him to deliver a letter in Frisco. He might send Daniel with it, but it would be better, perhaps, if he went himself.

So Captain Cleaveland went to his cabin for the letter, and, passing the mirror, looked in. He didn't like that tie as much as the light-colored silk one. It took some time to make the change and adjust the knot, and now he had rumpled his hair. He combed it smooth, brushed his clothes, shined his boots, and then stood once more before his mirror. Yes, he'd do. He looked well enough, and he felt pretty much a man.

He strode forward.

"That lower deck wants slicking up, Mr. Cleaveland," he said to his mate as he went by.

The business with Captain Fligg was soon settled, but Captain Cleaveland didn't see Mary. He lingered aboard the *Emma Prescott* on one pretext or another, but still he didn't see Mary. He *had* to see her. Well, here was Mrs. Lohn.

In spite of her husband's warning Mrs. Lohn wanted to assist in a romance. Mr. Lohn hadn't approved of the captain's attentions. "We promised to take Mary to her sister in San Francisco."

"We didn't know Providence would intervene, Henry."

"We don't know anything about the man."

"Tut, tut. He's a good man, a captain of a ship. Where will she ever get such another chance?"

"Her sister can give her every advantage. She'll not lack for offers of marriage. And there's plenty of time, since she's only sixteen. If Captain Cleaveland's intentions are honorable . . . . "

"Henry!"

"Oh, I have no doubt they are. Let him present himself to the McCloskeys. They are the ones to make such a decision."

"Now. Henry. You know how such things are. He'll go

to the other side of the world, and some other huz—some other girl'll get him. They always do."

And now that Mrs. Lohn saw the young captain approaching and saw his expression of gloom, she felt determined to act as Cupid. Together they planned all sorts of trips that Mary would enjoy.

10

IN THE days that followed they rode to Waikiki, "spouting water," where the breakers foam up on the beach. They saw the natives ride the surf. Mary had never seen such swimming.

They went to the old fort on Punch Bowl Hill that she had noticed as she first entered the harbor. On its rim were the fortifications and a flagstaff. Within the bowl was a green pasture where goats and cattle were grazing.

They rode past grass huts and taro patches to Diamond Head, about three miles east of Waikiki, where they stopped at a native dwelling to sample fish tied up in bundles of ti leaves. They heard the sea flowing through beds of queer-shaped lava, making guttural groans and moanings.

In the warm, bright evenings Mary and James walked hand in hand beneath the canopy of stars that stood out like jewels in the transparent atmosphere. Mary forgot about San Francisco. She forgot about the audience of gentlemen and ladies and sang for James in the starlight. Never had she sung so beautifully!

And they'd sit together on the deck of the *Emma Prescott* watching the bright light in the sky, a reflection from Mauna Loa. James told her about climbing to the crater of Kilauea on the neighboring island of Hawaii through a vast belt of woodland. He had seen bird's-nest ferns, spikes of red and brown flowers, and the rare birds that yielded from under each wing a single yellow feather that was kept exclusively for the cloaks of the Hawaiian kings. He had crept to the edge of the crater. Mary could see it all as he spoke.

But she liked best of all to hear about *his* island, the island of Martha's Vineyard, an idyllic land where he had always lived, and where he wanted to be whenever he was at home from sea. All the people knew each other and were friendly and good. Where he lived in the center of the island there was a pretty little village with a millstream and a white church where everyone went on Sundays. There were sheep and cows in the meadows. There were trout in the brooks, and the streams were all flecked with silver when the herring spawned in the spring. The young folks went to singing school and writing school. There would be parties and dances and sewing bees. There were quilting parties where the women spent the afternoon and the men joined them in the evening. There were sea captains aplenty, each with a big house and a fast horse or two. James meant to have all of these things some day.

And tonight as they sat on a balcony overlooking the

harbor he was telling her of his family—of his sisters, his other brother, his father and mother.

"Pa's so sure of himself," he said, "nothing Ma does makes a mite of difference. And Ma's full of fun. She can see a joke if there is one."

"He's homesick, for all his brave front," Mary thought. "He wants to see his mother, just as I want to see mine."

She felt like telling him about her mother, about her brothers and sisters, of their little home in Sydney. He'd never asked. He had been too busy telling about his interests. She had loved listening. Now she'd tell him. She'd tell him of her childhood joys and fears that mean so much as memories in later days. And she'd tell him what she had told no one else—about her hopes for fame in San Francisco—about the vision that had come to her of a glorious future, where by her singing she'd have the world at her feet. By her singing she'd change the whole course of her life.

She was about to tell him all these things. She turned toward him. His face was tense with passion.

"Mary!" His voice was husky.

She put her hand on his sleeve. "No, Captain Cleaveland, please. We each have separate ways . . . . "

"Not any more, Mary." James kissed her tenderly. "Not after that day on the Heights." He kissed her again. "Not after those precious hours together. We haven't had separate ways from the moment I saw you and heard you singing in the bow of the *Emma Prescott*."

He took her in his arms and kissed her hair and her eyes and her lips. Then he crushed her body against his.

Mary struggled no longer against fate. She knew that

5 6

such love could not be gainsaid. She stayed close to him, with her little turned-up nose sniffing the salt, musty smell of his coat. "You smell like the sea."

"You smell like an island—like getting back home—like new-mown grass and hay and sweet fern, grape blossoms, and wild roses."

But James's ideas were prone to turn practical. "We'll get married dear, in the Seaman's Bethel. I'll see Mr. Taylor about it in the morning."

Mary was silent.

James, made keen and sympathetic by his love, realized that something was troubling her. "What is it, darling?"

Mary felt like crying, she was so ashamed. She muffled her face against him. "I have nothing to wear for a wedding."

Tonight James was equal to any emergency. "I have just the thing," he said.

"You!" she almost laughed through her tears.

"Yes! I have some peachblow silk that I bought in China."

"But it has to be made up, and dressmakers take ever so long."

"Not always. We'll go tomorrow and find somebody who can fit you out like a queen and have you ready to set sail before the week is ended. Then we'll be off for the Vineyard!"

II

Now they were going home. Mary sat on the horse-hair sofa in the captain's cabin looking out of the little windows in the stern of the ship. Nothing was to be seen but the curling foam in the wake of the vessel and, beyond, the wide ocean. She could hear the swish and gurgle of the waves. She could hear the ocean above the pounding in her ears, above the rattling and banging and pulling of the ship. She could smell the sea.

She felt sick, but a glance at her ring steadied her—the thin band of yellow gold James had put on her finger at the Seaman's Bethel. She twisted it around on her fore-finger and took it off to look once again at the inscription inside. Just her initials, M. C., which now stood for Mary Cleaveland.

They brought to mind the little chapel in Honolulu where she had gone in the peachblow silk. James was waiting for her as she came up the aisle with Captain

Fligg. She saw him standing tall above his brother. She saw friendly faces on either side—Mr. and Mrs. Lohn and all the captains whose ships were in port. A few of the captains' wives were there. She began to lose her self-consciousness, to forget herself, even though she heard the Chinese silk rustling as she went up the aisle. She thought only of James standing there waiting for her. Then she saw the chaplain of the Bethel, book in hand. The Reverend Mr. Taylor, not a priest, but a minister! She thought of her mother, of her father, of the great Catholic cathedral in Sydney. But she did not allow her mind to dwell on them. This was James's way, and she would be his wife. She looked up at him as he put the ring on her finger, looked up and smiled.

The pitch of the vessel jerked her head and brought her back to the *Mary Wilder*. She reached for a little box and took out the crucifix she kept there, and, holding it in her hand, she lay back on the sofa. But she hid it quickly and glanced toward the door, for James was coming. She knew his step. She always knew when James was coming.

Mary sat up, but the roll of the ship made her feel queer. She lay down again and smiled only the ghost of a smile when the cabin door opened. Oh, dear! She didn't want to be a care to James, when he already had on his mind the whole weight of sailing a ship with a cargo worth ever so much—and shorthanded, too. She tried again to sit up.

"Why don't you lie down on the bed, Mary? There'll come a rough sea, and then where'll you be? You'll be pitched right off that horsehair sofa on to the floor."

He held out his hand, and she rose. But as she got up

the crucifix slipped from the folds of her gown. He picked it up, looking serious, and pointing to his well-worn Bible on the shelf said, "There, dear, is the root of the whole matter. You don't need these little images!" Then he laughed at her tragic face. "Keep it! But don't let Ma see it!"

He helped her to the bed and spread over her the beautiful shawl he had brought from China for his mother. He stood looking at her. A tiny little thing! He'd have to be careful of her. Huddled up there on the sofa—trying to sit up when he came in! What pretty hair she had! It was dark around her white face. It waved in little ringlets over her damp forehead and fell back loosely on the pillow. He wished he dared touch it.

With a ship under him he could brave anything, even the thunderstorms his mother had taught him to dread. He could beat right through a gale and think nothing of it. He could knock down a brawny sailor if he overstepped the bounds of ship's discipline. But he wanted to touch Mary's hair, and he was afraid. She looked so white with the dark shadow of her lashes on her cheeks.

He knelt down beside her and took her hand in both of his.

Mary opened her eyes. They were deep blue-gray. The color flooded back into her cheeks. The red and blue-gray flowers in the Chinese embroidery seemed to come alive.

She saw that he was kneeling. "No, James! I won't lie here so good for nothing."

They stood together. He put his arms around her and kissed her.

"It seemed all the time, James, as though there was something beyond us, something more powerful than we, drawing us together. Is love like that?"

"Yes."

"But I think the harder we struggle against it, the more glorious is the moment we give in to it."

"Now we'll guard love carefully, Mary, knowing its value."

"We'll take what comes, won't we, James," she spoke as if reassuring herself. "And never think how different things might have been?"

" 'Forgetting those things which are behind, and reaching forth unto those things which are before,' " James quoted.

"We'll not look back and wish things different!"

"Forward together, all sails set!"

James glanced at the telltale compass in the ceiling over his bed. "What's that fool doing with the ship?" He turned, strode to the door, and went up the ladder two steps at a time.

All sails set! She had married a sea captain! From now on her life would be bound up with the ocean, the ocean that she feared and hated.

She glanced at the compass, steady now that James was on deck. She smiled ruefully. She must share her man with the sea.

And now James was taking her to the other side of the world. It would be many years before she could make her visit to San Francisco. They were going back through the South Pacific, around Cape Horn, spending Christmas wallowing in the trough of the heavy seas, up through the

South Atlantic, across the equator again. They were pushed onward by the trade winds, washed by gentle rains, becalmed in a glassy sea, and battered by storms.

It was not until the spring that they arrived at the port of New Bedford, the first time they had touched land since they left Honolulu nearly six months before.

12

After the long journey from the Pacific, the stay at New Bedford had been a brief respite while James settled up the necessary details at the customhouse. Now they were on the water again. This little craft, this steamer *Telegraph*, bobbed about on the waves so that it seemed worse than rounding the Horn. Mary could see land all around, which helped. There were ships everywhere—clippers speeding by, schooners laden with lumber, clay, bricks. There were more than a dozen whalers. Here was one with the sails blackened from the tryworks. James snorted disapproval, "Couldn't even dress up to come to port."

James left his wife while he went to gam with the captain. Other captains accepted James, glad to admit to their ranks the son of Captain Henry Cleaveland. He was a fine upstanding man in his own right, fearless and keen. He was honest and God-fearing, as Vineyard tradition prescribed, and he had a touch of the diplomat, mixed with quick wit and straightforward manner—a rare combination.

He heard the latest news of the Vineyard and told Captain Barker the news of the fleet at the Sandwich Islands. James basked in the warmth of his new importance. The last time he was at home he was only a first mate.

"The ship *Constitution*, my brother's ship," Captain Barker said, "arrived at Holmes's Hole the end of last month, bound to Nantucket. They had difficulty in getting her over the bar at the harbor, even though they took off much of her cargo at Holmes's Hole. Shipping is about all done for in Nantucket." Captain Barker shook his head disconsolately. "They can use the men that have been bred to whaling, but the port has served its period of usefulness. Now it's done for."

"There are plenty of Nantucket captains still in the Pacific if you want to know where to find them. They are good whalers." James was willing to give the devil his due, and Captain Barker came from Nantucket.

"What grounds you been working these last few years?"

"I've been cruising pretty close to California, to see what was going to happen there."

"You got to California in the Gold Rush?" queried Captain Barker.

"Yes. Father was master of the *Niantic* and Sylvanus, Daniel, and I each had a berth on her. When we put in at Valparaíso there was all this talk about California, so Father had the ship fitted for passengers and took a lot of them from Panama up to the gold fields. The men went off hunting gold so fast that they never waited to be paid off and left hardly so much as a Frenchman to man the *Niantic*."

"Didn't you go, too?"

"Certainly. But we were no hands at digging in the earth. We came back again to go to sea. We thought 'twould soon blow over and the rest would join us. But we couldn't get enough men to sail a ship, so we sold the *Niantic* at a good profit. They beached her and used her as a storeship and warehouse. More shipshape, she was, than those sham-built structures they put up on shore. What a city that was! No place for an honest man."

"Where did you get the brig you just brought in?"

"We bought the *Mary Wilder* because she had half the tonnage, and we figured if we could get over to the Sandwich Islands we could pick up a few Kanakas. With the family and a few others we made it, then to China for goods to trade in San Francisco. We bought silks, embroideries, furniture, and the like and brought them back to the coast. They'd have bought anything."

"Then what did you do?" Captain Barker was reliving the days when he was in the thick of things.

"In San Francisco the whalers were still carpenters. Couldn't blame them, with wages so high. But the buildings looked it." James chuckled, though he deplored the folly and dishonesty of men. "Then Father and Sylvanus took another small merchantman, and I commanded the *Mary Wilder* with Daniel as mate and a mighty small crew. (We had three seamen and a cook.) I tell you we worked to keep her going!"

"Kind of tough sleddin'."

6 5

"I've been aboard a whaler when there were thirty or forty to man her. It's a comedown when there are only six, counting master and cook."

"I declare, I don't see how you did it." Captain Barker studied his course. "Where did you get the cargo?"

"At Honolulu. We took her over there to fit out and get more men before rounding Cape Horn. We have 26,000 gallons of oil from the ship *Jeanette*, 20,000 from the *William Thompson*. Captain Jernegan sent some bone by the barque *Helen*, too. He was having pretty good luck and is staying another season."

"Who else did you see there?"

"I saw Captain Dexter of the *Chile* and Captain Smith of the *Falcon* at the Islands. Ship *Callao*, Captain Sisson, arrived at New Bedford two days ahead of me."

"Yes, the *Telegraph* came alongside of her. I saw Captain Covell, too."

"Yes. He came in the same day I did."

James looked up and started. "Why, here we are most to Woods Hole!" He went to join Mary.

They were going through a narrow opening where the land made close to them and where rocks jutted out in front of them.

"That's Woods Hole we're coming to, Mary. A bad place, if you don't know the channel. You see that old house over there? No, no, to starboard. One of the Cleavelands built that house, they say, long before I was born. I don't rightly know which one of them it was, but probably my great-grandfather. It's on Nonamesset, so close to Naushon it's almost a part of it. Those are the Elizabeth Islands lying along there. Bartholomew

Gosnold named them for Queen Elizabeth, though some say these islands were named differently." And he told her the legend of the three sisters: "Elizabeth, the eldest, was homely so she got the Elizabeth Islands. Martha, the beauty, got Martha's Vineyard, but when it came to little Nancy, there wasn't much left but that island to the southeast, so Nan-tuck-et." He laughed heartily.

Mary had already found that he liked to joke at the expense of the sister island. She was to find later that once on the Vineyard, "Holmes's Holers" and "Old-towners" were fruitful sources of ridicule for James's family. In West Tisbury the best people, according to Mary Ann, were Cleavelands and Athearns, and in the intimate family circle not all of these were immune.

They waited a long time at Woods Hole. Freight was being hurried aboard on heavy hand trucks. The men were working fast to get the mass of bales and crates on board. As they ran down the gangplank their trucks bounced along ahead of them, and the iron wheels rumbled across the rough planks of the wharf.

Gray gulls and slender terns with orange bills wheeled in the air and swooped to the water for bits of food or unwary fish. Their cries and the sounds from the dock mingled with the surge of the water as it swirled through the weeds and barnacles of the wharf piles.

The sun had been bright and the water sparkling. Now it was getting overcast, with a chilly wind springing up. There was more water to cross. It looked like a nasty stretch of sea, too, where the wind could sweep right through.

James pointed out the Vineyard lying there. To Mary

it was merely land that she could fasten her eyes on to keep from being seasick. To James it was home, pregnant with memories of pranks and sugar cookies, fishing and fighting, parties and church, school and holiday time, his mother and sisters—home. His eyes shone, his voice was eager. He had been patient a long time, but now he was within sight of home.

Mary nestled her hand into his. "Do you think they'll like me, James?" she asked.

James's hand stiffened. Well, that was a question! Funny he hadn't thought of that before, or if he had, he had put it aside to consider later. His mother usually liked to be consulted about his moves—but law! He wouldn't consult anybody if he wanted to take a wife, and it certainly was time he was married.

There was 'Phrony Cathcart. A nice girl! Mother was kind of set on her. Mother had things pretty well planned for him to marry her. However, a man's mother couldn't settle those matters. He'd given 'Phrony a ring, but he had forgotten how it looked on her finger. He had forgotten her bright brown eyes, her dignified bearing. He had seen her all his life, but he had forgotten her. But always, as long as he lived, he would remember Mary as she looked in the bow of the *Emma Prescott* in Honolulu, standing there singing that lilting song.

He looked down at her, thoughtfully.

"You're sweet enough for anybody to like," he answered.

The whistle blew a strident blast. The dock crew ran for the lines leading to the gangplank, and with a rush they hauled it to the wharf.

68

Bells jangled in the engine room and the paddle wheels beat the water to a froth.

James led Mary to the railing. "That's good seamanship," he conceded.

As the steamer moved its bow slowly around toward the harbor entrance, paddle wheel, rudder, and lines overcame the strong tide pull. The heavy hawser slackened at the stern and was taken in on the wharf. The bowline stretched and creaked around the piles and cramped into the bitts as it was slowly paid out. When it seemed that the stern would crash into the piling there was a shout from the bridge, and both lines splashed into the water. Bells rang, and the full thrust of the paddles drove the *Telegraph* out into the tide rip of the Hole. Soon she was out in Vineyard Sound, where the force of the wind pulled at her to hold her back.

As they shifted their course the wood smoke blew down into their faces. James said it was almost as bad as the tryworks, but Mary had no experience of that. She didn't mind the smell of wood smoke when it wasn't too dense.

They went up into the bow. It seemed rougher, but the air was clear. Sea gulls cruised along beside them, flying a little, then sailing on stiffened pinions, looking slyly with their bright, beady eyes, then sneering at them. "A ship without wings, ha, ha."

"They aren't used to steamers, yet," Mary thought.

If Mary kept her eyes on the land she felt better. The island looked gloomy now with the clouds hovering over it, except where the sunlight shone on that point at a little distance, picking out the queer-shaped cedar trees, a

69

white lighthouse, and two or three buildings nestled into the slope.

"Godfrey!" James exclaimed. "Just get a whiff of that air! Apple blossoms! You get the land smell in other places and it's full of palm trees or oleanders or some such alien thing."

Mary thought of her home in Sydney. This island would be alien to her.

James didn't notice her preoccupation. "Here it's sweetfern, bay, wild roses, grapevine. Now that it's early you get the lilacs and apple blossoms. Smell 'em?"

"It *is* nice."

"There's a great mass of purple lilacs at Aunt Becky's, right by the northeast corner of the house—and cherry trees! There's a row of big ones to the eastward, so big you couldn't get both arms around the trunks. They rumble in the spring, they're so full of bees. Then there's the early pear tree. Summer mornings I used to get up to get the pears before Aunt Becky did. Beyond that, all over the crown of the hill, is the apple orchard. It's prettier than Father's place, it's so old and settled. I'd like to own it. I have always wanted it for mine."

"Your great-grandfather's place?"

"Yes. Squire George Athearn, they called him."

They were in the shelter of the island now.

"That's West Chop, where the cedar trees are. East Chop is over yonder. There's a grove of oak trees there where they hold the camp meetings. Every summer crowds come from off. They have ever since I was a boy. They gather around and listen to preaching from morning to night, sitting down every once in a while to a meal of cold victuals in the hot sun. Tents spring up like mushrooms and cover the whole place. Captain Barker says it's still going strong, with more tents expected this summer. They'll be putting a steamboat landing there first thing you know. At one time there were twenty-five ministers there at once. That's too many for one place; there's sure to be trouble. It's like having all those missionaries in the Sandwich Islands."

They were steaming into the harbor, where boats of all sorts were moored. Along the shore there were fish houses, storehouses, blacksmith shops, carpenter shops—a city in miniature. Behind the shore rose the higher land with the roofs of stately houses showing gray and weather worn or painted shipshape among the trees.

The *Telegraph* had slowed down. Sailors stood ready with casting lines coiled in their hands. They could see a crowd of people on the wharf. It seemed as though the whole town had come down to see the boat come in. "They always do," James explained. "These Holmes's Holers have nothing else to do. The whalers are beginning to come in now, too, and they want to hear the news. Most of them have an interest in some ship or other."

He recognized familiar faces. There was Warren. There was Mr. Bodfish. Funny he couldn't see Mother. At least Daniel should be there, for he had come on ahead, while the captain transacted business in New Bedford. Then he saw John, and John saw him. The black face lighted with a flashing smile. James turned from the bow of the boat and rushed below, leaving Mary to follow breathlessly.

71

13

S HE was on land again. Mary hoped she would always be thankful enough each time she set foot on the land. She would soon recover her spirits, which had drooped unaccountably as the clouds had swept over the island before her when she had been on the steamer.

People crowded around, glad to see James, curious about this woman with him, for word had traveled fast since the *Mary Wilder* had arrived in New Bedford. It was said that James was bringing with him a woman "from off."

"Your wife? Pleased to meet ya." And lest he appear too eager about affairs strictly personal, this lean Yankee with eyes clear from sea vision hastened to add, "Have much of a cargo?"

Relatives, friends, neighbors, business associates greeted James and bowed to Mary or stared in astonishment.

She would always remember the smile of one of the

cousins in that sea of curious faces. He helped her to the carriage, and they stood near, talking. James's father, he said, was own cousin to his father. He wished they would come home with him, only he knew there'd be no keeping James here in Holmes's Hole. He'd want to get up island. He hoped she and James would come down once in a while.

James approached just then with bags and boxes. The big negro held her little pigskin trunk in one hand. The other things would be left here until they could be called for in the truck wagon—the teakwood chair he had bought in China, the boxes of tea and preserved fruits, the big bunch of bananas from Honolulu, the silks.

He piled things in the back seat, then helped Mary in beside them. He and John climbed in the front. The negro clucked to the horse and grinned broadly. Mr. James looked good to him.

Lawdy, Lawd, how good Mr. James's father had looked to him when he finally decided to let him stay on board ship. He'd been mighty cross when he found him, shivering in the hold, a stowaway. He looked as grumpy as an old bear, seein' him there where he didn't belong, but he never lit on him, as some of 'em would 'a' done. "Yes, Captain Henry sho' saved this Nigger's life."

James broke into his meditations. "How did Daniel get home yesterday? How's Mother? What? She's been acting queer?" James knew the symptoms. His mother was seriously displeased. James kept quiet, thinking.

Black John told him the news of the village. Poor Aunt

Avis died. It wasn't his place to say much about it, but 'twas his idea that she died of a broken heart. Had they heard of the beautiful Swedish singer, Jenny Lind? Everybody was talking about her. There was a big wedding in the village last fall—Miss Ann Johnson was married to Mr. Henry L. Whiting. A few days later James Athearn of Scrubby Neck was married to Miss Margaret Pease, but there wasn't so much of a to-do about that. His father and brothers were expected most any time. You never knew when these folks would show up. There was talk all over of letting the slaves go free, only the Southerners didn't want to do that 'cause they had the slaves, and the Northerners had no slaves to speak of, so they was willing to let 'em go.

James began once more to ask questions. A place changes after three or four years.

The horse took his way along. John didn't urge him, perhaps because he knew it was useless until the old horse could smell the oats of home, perhaps because he enjoyed having Captain James as an audience and wished to take advantage of the opportunity. The air was so soft and sleepy feeling one couldn't expect the horse to go fast. In spite of the slowness of the pace, they soon left the village behind and entered a narrow but well-worn road. Scrub oaks closed in on either side of them. Scrub oaks extended as far as the eye could see, stubby bushes, with a few larger oaks standing stark and beaten by the wind. Occasionally a pine tree loomed green but gnarled and covered with small gray cones. Otherwise, the eye could see little but a pastel sea of pink and gray. The scrub oaks weren't ever green, although it was the middle of May.

7 4

The horse jogged on, moving up and down as much as forward. Mary drew a deep breath. The leaves had an acrid smell. There was dust, too, and harness leather, and the musty sea smell of the bags beside her. That, at any rate, was familiar. It made her homesick for the *Mary Wilder.* She suddenly dreaded meeting these new people in this strange, out of the way place, living way in here in the bush.

On and on, mile after mile, nothing to be seen but the drab scrub oaks, touched shamefacedly with pink.

Once in a while James would turn around. "Right over there," he said, "is the best place in the plains for blueberries. One year I got them so thick you could scoop them up in handfuls."

"Could you find the place again?" Mary wondered. "It all looks so much alike."

On and on they went. The sky grew darker, making the oaks look duller in the dim light. A few drops of rain fell. As they passed a swampy hollow James pointed it out and said, "There'll be pinkletinks here this evening!"

"Pinkletinks?"

"Yes, a kind of young frog. They make you feel sure of spring."

The way turned sharply into a broader, freer road, with comparatively tall trees beside it. They reached the top of a steep incline and there before them was spread a panorama of distant hills, woods, and fields and a dainty little village. Quite close was a group of houses.

"There's Squire George's, Mary. That's the house I mean to own some day. See it, sitting there big among those apple trees, a nice pasture, good land to till."

The horse, sensing the nearness of supper, hurried a little. "Get up," shouted James encouragingly. "We haven't struck a dead calm here. Get along!" John, taking the hint, slapped the reins against the brown flank.

"There's Jesse Pease's. There's John Manter's. Who's that swarming out of Squire George's?"

"Mistah Joseph Nickerson's done bought that place and is rearin' himself a fambly."

Well, Joseph Nickerson might be persuaded to bring up his family elsewhere. He'd come here from off. He had no reason for living there. He had no right to it except that he'd bought it. His ancestors hadn't dug the soil here, fenced the place, cut down trees, bargained with the Indians, and planned a community. Godfrey! If anyone deserved to smoke his pipe here, it was one of Simon Athearn's descendants. That old cuss did his part in this American democracy.

"There's William Luce's." He'd met William at the Sandwich Islands. William had married Betsy Vincent before he sailed. James wondered whether she was living here. The place looked as though somebody was.

"There's Caroline Luce's to the starboard." Smoke was coming out of the chimney. "She's cooking a good supper, you may depend on that."

"Rotch's store!" There were teams hitched up there, seven or eight of them. One of the men spied him. "James," they called, as they came piling out of the doorway. His schoolmates. They'd been to sea together as young boys. They'd been courting together. Now some of them were settled down, some of them waiting for the

7 6

MARY ANN CLEAVELAND—*at about forty years*

opportunity to go another voyage. They knew he was in a hurry to get home, and anyway the horse was taking the bit in his teeth, for without urging he suddenly turned the corner and went flying down the road. Home was just beyond.

The gate was open. The horse turned in and stopped in front of the barn.

Just then the west door of the house burst open and two big girls ran out and threw themselves into James's arms. He could hardly believe they were his little sisters. Well, it was nearly four years since he'd seen them.

They turned shyly and kissed James's bride. Mary felt they would always be friendly.

But in the doorway, nearly blocking it, stood a forbidding figure, a woman, large, dignified, handsome in spite of the fact that the corners of her mouth drooped, handsome in spite of the steely glint in her eyes.

Mary reached for her husband's hand. He took hers and they went forward like two young culprits. Would she let them come in? What should they do if she turned them away? They could feel the rain in their faces now. They could hear the monotonous pounding and surging from the south, the noise that islands make when you pass them in a ship—when they sound a warning to keep off.

They went forward and up on the stone step. The woman bent down and from her point of vantage coolly kissed James.

"My wife, Mother," he said.

James's mother bowed formally and, turning, went into the house. James and his wife followed.

That was the bride's reception.

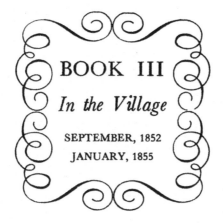

BOOK III

In the Village

SEPTEMBER, 1852
JANUARY, 1855

14

THEY were going down the Plains Road to Holmes's Hole. The scrub oaks were gray now, but a different shade from the pastels of spring. They were the color of well-worn things.

But the plains no longer looked dull, for amongst the sober oaks plumes of goldenrod were waving and the huckleberry brush flamed scarlet. Overhead the sky was bright and warm, but close to the horizon hovered the mist of Indian summer, and in the hollows last night's frost still lingered.

They rode on silently. Mary could see the dark hair curling under her husband's hat. She could see his strong, fine profile as he turned towards his brother on the seat beside him. He was the only one of the family whose mouth turned up at the corners. She liked sitting here where she could watch him. She knew her mother-in-law had foregone the pleasure of sitting with Daniel, who was driving, and had taken the seat back here to keep Mary from sitting beside James. But she was glad. They had said all that could be said last night when they had been alone. This woman could never take away those hours.

. . .

James had been so happy that she had fallen in with his mood and had forgotten to be sad. He had been lifted to a plane beyond her ken, but she had dropped her own feelings, like leaden weights, to follow. He was going out, as captain of the *Mary Wilder*, to do battle with the wind and sea, to catch whales, figuratively bringing them back to lay at the feet of his lady. His previous trips were unimportant. Now he was going for Mary, for money to buy a home where Mary could be queen, where she would always be waiting for him at the end of a long, hard voyage.

He had made her feel the sea as he would feel it, lapping, lapping, urging the winged ship on to make their fortune. Mary had lived for months on shipboard. She could picture the many moods of the sea. She could see James facing into the elements.

He had made her feel the wind in the rigging, not as a destructive force, but as he heard it, a power helping them.

He had made her feel his authority as captain giving commands to a whaleboat's crew. She had felt the excitement of the chase.

When he grew sad at leaving her, it had been her turn to raise his spirits. She had been merry and had told him that two years would pass quickly, when he'd be back again. They'd be together with life to live intensely once more.

She had lain beside him, satisfied that he loved her, smiling as she sank into sleep with her head on his broad shoulder and his arms around her.

She had wakened, feeling herself crushed hard against him. She had tried to move, but James in his sleep had only grasped her the tighter as though nothing could take her from him, so she stayed there, quietly enjoying the discomfort. Nothing, not even the ocean, could deprive her of last night.

In spite of confidence in his voyage, James was not without misgivings about leaving Mary. He wished his mother had "taken to her," but they'd get along. Women had their tiffs, but they got over them. There was nothing that could be done about it. He was a whaler, and he had to go to sea. Sea was no place for a woman. Well, the Cleavelands were lucky. He'd fill the ship full and be back in two or three years.

Mary thought of the possibilities for entertaining herself. She had had good times with James this summer, pleasures modified, it was true, by the uncompromising hostility of the mistress of the house. The evening parties held there had been spoiled for her because James would be occupied talking to the men, telling about this ship and that and such and such a topsail or jib boom. She would try to do her part towards entertaining the women, but her mother-in-law would always contrive, when James was occupied, to make her feel an outsider. There were times when she felt even James considered her out of her element.

One evening when the women, led by Mary Ann, ignored her, she listened to the men talking about Cape

Horn. She knew that subject. She went over and joined them, joined in with their conversation.

James looked stern, but the other men had smiled at some bright saying, and the tension around James's mouth had lessened. She had made pretense of being asleep, however, when he came to bed, so he couldn't take her to task for her conduct, which she knew to be unorthodox, and she'd been careful not to encroach again. But she knew she had allies among the men and also among some of the women who had felt Mary Ann's caustic tongue.

Perhaps, Mary thought, her mother-in-law's attitude would change when James was gone. It must be hard for a woman to have sons, little boys who depended on her, who came to her with everything—their little troubles and their joys. Then they grew bigger and went to sea— went with their father and became his children. The next time she saw them they'd be swaggering men—not men really, but make-believe ones. When she recovered from that, they'd come home and be sweet to her, and thoughtful, and she'd think she had her sons back again. But it didn't last. Each one went to some young woman and was hers. Her own brothers hadn't been much comfort at home.

When James had gone, surely his mother and his wife could work together, waiting till he came again.

"When James had gone!" Those were the words that kept recurring, making an undertone of sadness that she couldn't quite comprehend as yet. She felt as people did about a funeral, not sad really until it was all over; then the loneliness came.

Now she actually felt like singing. The first lines of an old ballad ran through her mind:

You are going far away, far away from poor Janet.
There is no one left to love me now and you, too, may forget.

If she were alone she'd sing. She'd sing until the tears rolled down her cheeks, until the weight lifted—then she'd be brave and smile good-by.

In the midst of this thought she couldn't help wondering what the effect would be if she were suddenly to sing. James might remember that he first fell in love with her as she was singing in the bow of the ship entering Honolulu. He could understand singing with joy. She had heard James sing, not melodiously but joyously, when the wind and salt spray beat in his face. But singing because your heart was weighted down would be a different thing to James. As for his mother and Daniel, they would think she was crazy. They never knew of anyone's singing except to entertain company or sing those doleful hymns in church.

She looked ahead at James's sturdy back. Silently she continued the song:

With your gun upon your shoulder and your bayonet by your side
You'll be courting some fair lady and making her your bride.

No, she wasn't afraid James would forget her. She was sure of his love.

Mary looked sidewise at her mother-in-law. She was gazing ahead at her sons, at James especially. She wouldn't see him again for two or three years, perhaps never. Mary didn't know then that every time the ocean moaned and beat upon the South Shore Mrs. Cleaveland would say, "A bad night for the sailors!" and would pace the floor restlessly. It didn't matter that her men were miles away from the storm, in another ocean. To her the pounding of the surf was symbolic of trouble at sea. Mary did know that the older woman was suffering, even as she herself was. She felt like putting out her hand for contact with another human being with the same weight in her heart. Mary could forgive the slights and embarrassments, the deliberate misunderstandings. But the back of the woman beside her was uncompromisingly stiff, the head high, the features proud. Mary turned away. Mrs. Henry Cleaveland neither asked for quarter nor gave it.

15

THEY had to wait at the wharf in Holmes's Hole. John Pease was there with his stagecoach from Edgartown. Oliver Mayhew was there with the stage from up island, but the boat hadn't come from Nantucket. James talked with them all, and they were eager to talk to him. Glamorous, romantic, adventurous men, these sea captains. Young women stood looking and smiling. Boys stood agape, eager for the time when they, too, might go to sea. Old captains sunned themselves in the shelter, dignified, satisfied with their pasts, and the sparkle in their eyes told that they were reliving, with the young man, the good old days of sailing.

"Young fellers are having it easy these days. Take it when we went to sea, Sirson, privateers a hounding us, Britishers hauling the men right off our ships, and the war spoiling the shipping." Their memories went back to 1812.

Sirson shifted his chew of tobacco. "Couldn't *spoil* the business. Folks had to have the oil."

"What do you think of this new-fangled oil, petroleum?"

Sirson spat before he answered, "Never make a go of it. Coal oil ain't the same as sperm!"

They walked over and shook hands with James. "A good voyage to you, Captain," they said and went back to stand by the freight shed, pleased with their diplomacy in addressing such a young man by the highest title of his honorable calling.

Meanwhile James's wife and mother stood together, forgotten in the rush of attending to the sea chests and duffel bags. The *Telegraph* was blowing its ugly whistle, and Captain Barker, not satisfied with the power of its blast, was shouting in his quarter-deck voice, "All aboard!" James came over to kiss his mother and his wife. Mary smiled and kissed him. She didn't trust herself to speak, but her eyes said simply and seriously, "A good voyage, James, so you'll come back to me soon."

Soon! Two years would be the soonest she could expect him. Two years from her life. She'd be nineteen before he ever could come back again.

They rattled a few last pieces of freight aboard the *Telegraph*. Mary saw James step in amongst the throng with his head held high above the others, and then he disappeared. She saw him again up on the bridge with Captain Barker.

Then the engine started; the paddle wheels churned up foam against the wharf piles. Mary almost shouted, "Don't go yet!" But they had pulled in the gangplank and cast off the hawsers. They were moving away. She felt she must do something to keep him. Then she saw his face with all its eagerness gone, made sad by her pitiful grief. She flashed a quick smile and stood there, calmly letting her handkerchief flutter. He was too far away now to see the tears streaming down her cheeks.

She could scarcely see him now, only she knew he was there, so she kept on waving. The *Telegraph* was making headway among the sailing vessels in the harbor. It was growing smaller and smaller until she could no longer distinguish the figures on the bridge. Then the steamer disappeared behind the gnarled old cedar trees on the tip of West Chop.

Mary shook back the tears and turned, feeling spent and forlorn. She looked desperately at her mother-in-law, the only one to whom she could turn. She found, not sympathy, not tolerance, not even grief, but bitterness, in her eyes and in the lines around her mouth.

"Now, young woman, while James is gone, you are going to get over some of your notions. Since he's gone and married you, which he had no business to do, I'm going to make a fitting wife of you. Then, when he comes back, he won't be so sorry he's done it."

Mary stamped her foot on the ground beside the carriage. "He isn't sorry he married me." But when her anger was combined with grief she couldn't control her tears. They streamed down her face afresh.

"Well, what are you crying for? You married a sea captain. You can't keep him tied to your apron strings."

"I didn't expect to keep him at home."

"Well, you couldn't have done it if you'd tried. I'll tell you one thing. I've summered 'em and wintered 'em, and I've never yet seen a sea captain that could make a living on land."

16

THE post office was not far away, just down the lane and around the corner opposite the store. Old Willard Luce was postmaster—a feeble old man, but unless a ship had recently come into port it didn't take him long to sort out the mail, except on Friday nights when the *Gazette* came.

Mary went there each day. And each day she came back empty-handed. She tried to come in quietly and go up to her room, but Mrs. Cleaveland usually managed to detain her.

"How's Caroline Luce?" she'd ask.

"Is she ill?"

"Mercy! How should I know? *I* don't hang around there."

And again, "How's Caroline Luce?"

Then Mary realized that Mrs. Theodor Luce, the postmaster's daughter-in-law, had come from off island, too. She had come to work in Bradley's factory down by the millpond, and Theodor, not deterred by her lack of social graces, had married her. Now Mrs. Cleaveland was bracketing Mary with Caroline Luce.

Mary's Irish temper and her spirit of justice rose. Even if Mrs. Luce was common, she was at least kind. Mary managed, just in time, to think of her mother's admonition to act "like a little lady," and answered calmly, "Mrs. Caroline Luce always speaks very kindly to me."

"I dare say." Anything could be read into those three words. But the subject was dropped.

The next time she came in the kitchen seemed full of big men. Mary sat down quietly near the door, but her mother-in-law had seen her. "Where have *you* been?" she asked.

Mrs. Cleaveland knew, of course, but Mary answered, "To the post."

"You're in the habit, I suppose, of getting plenty of mail in Port Jackson?" Mrs. Cleaveland must have considered it more insulting to call Sydney by its former name, for she always did so.

"It never mattered in Sydney."

Then James's father came to the rescue. "You can't expect a letter so soon, my dear. Sometimes it's months before you speak a ship going in the right direction."

"Well, Pa, you know about Cap'n Folger from Nantucket." Daniel spoke up.

"Cap'n Folger? Cap'n Abijah Folger?"

"I dunno whether 'twas him—but one of 'em. He just got married and went on a voyage. He'd been gone about three weeks—about off the Azores, he was—when the lookout calls, 'There she blows!' 'Where away?' says the cap'n. 'Two points off the lea bow.' They change course and head for him, then. 'Lower away!' shouts the cap'n. Just then he sights a brig makin' sail for the north'ard. Cap'n Folger pushes the mate aside and jumps into the boat. 'Make sail for yonder brig,' he commands. They signal the brig, and she, thinking they are in distress, heaves to. The cap'n boards her. 'See this letter gets to Nantucket,' he begs. Then he comes back to go whaling, but the whale they have sighted is gone."

"What was in the letter?" Mary asked in astonishment.

"I dunno for sure what was in the letter, but I heard tell that this captain went around with verses in his pocket all ready for his bride, and whenever he saw a ship headed for home he hailed her."

Mary was quiet. She knew the story was told for her benefit. She wished she hadn't asked any questions about the incident. Daniel was dramatic with his stories, and none of the family, not even James, could resist the opportunity of telling a good story, no matter at whose expense.

Usually Daniel was sympathetic and kind. He had known her before any of these others had seen her, so he felt almost responsible in a way. All of the men were nice when Mrs. Cleaveland was not around. Mary tried to be a jolly companion and to keep her sadness for her own room. She was tiny and pretty and had such a sweet voice and merry laugh that the boys liked to be with her. But none of these attributes endeared her to her mother-in-law.

Mary liked Captain Henry Cleaveland, James's father.

He was a quiet man, taking the storms of his wife's disposition as he took the storms of the ocean, with calmness and fortitude. He'd no more think of opposing his wife than he'd think of running counter to a northeast gale. When a man has been at the helm of a whaling vessel either he carries on with his usual authority and orders the household about, or else he takes the attitude that he has had his turn aboard ship, let someone else manage here. Henry Cleaveland was successful at sea. His men admired and respected him. He could command instant obedience by force of character, without a curse or a blow. And he'd catch whales, too

The captain made no attempt to interfere with his wife's treatment of Mary. He knew he could accomplish little now, and probably matters would be worse for his intervention when he was again at sea. But he would smile understandingly, and that helped Mary over many a bad place.

The two girls loved Mary. Their mother paid little attention to them, except to see that they had plenty to eat. Addie listened enraptured to the stories that Mary told, and Eliza would take Mary's arm, and they would walk out together.

"Let's go to the post office, Eliza."

"Yes. It's time for the paper, anyway."

They went down the lane arm in arm singing a little song that Mary had taught the girls:

> *Oh, dear, what can the matter be?*
> *Oh, dear, what can the matter be?*
> *Oh, dear, what can the matter be?*
> *Johnny's so long at the fair?*

He promised to buy me a basket of roses.
He promised to buy me a basket of posies.
He promised to buy me a bunch of blue ribbon
To tie up my bonnie brown hair.

They entered the post office pink cheeked and smiling and saw there men standing in solemn rows reading the newspaper. Over Mr. Manter's shoulder Mary saw a black-bordered column in the *Vineyard Gazette*. She felt sure the *Mary Wilder* had sunk, that the island was in mourning for James.

"Mr. Luce, please may I have the paper?" She forced her voice to sound natural. With trembling fingers she started to open it.

"Don't!" Eliza said. "Mother is always the first to read the *Gazette*."

"I can't help it, Eliza. I must know what that means."

Eliza helped her, and together they found the black-bordered item. Daniel Webster had died.

With a sigh of relief Mary folded up the paper and prepared to face Mrs. Cleaveland's wrath or her bitter wit. Mary didn't know which was worse.

17

So often Mary had heard James praise his mother's cooking—her pumpkin pies, her apple dumplings, her doughnuts! She wished she could learn how to make such things, to surprise James when he came back.

"Mother Cleaveland," she asked meekly, "will you teach me how to make pie?"

Mrs. Cleaveland was surprised, but still not ready to cooperate. She had always enjoyed hearing her men praise her pies, taking great mouthfuls to make up for years of privation and saying, "Godfrey, Ma! Nobody knows how to make pies like yours." Still, all girls ought to be able to make something in the way of a pie. She guessed the competition wouldn't be very keen. But she hesitated. "Where was your own mother, I'd like to know?"

"We used to get pies from the pieman. He used to come around with a tray on his head, calling,

Apple, mutton, and kidney pies—
All 'ot, 'ere, all 'ot.

Mary strutted around the kitchen, in imagination back in Sydney, selling pies as she had seen the pieman do, calling again in her musical voice the vendor's cry:

Apple, mutton, and kidney pies—
All 'ot, 'ere, all 'ot.

"My land! What a heathen country!"

"They were good pies, but not as good as yours."

"Well, get out the flour, the lard, the salt, and a little mite of water—cold, right out of the well."

Mary drew water, though she might have called John. She got out the supplies. She was humming as she worked.

"Now, take a large bowl and put in flour."

"How much shall I put in?"

"Fill it half full."

"Maybe I'd better make just one first."

"One's not a particle of use. Two's a small recipe."

"Is that right?"

"A speck of salt, and now shortening. You want it so's it just blends and feels right between your fingers."

Mary mixed it vigorously. She got flour on her nose and in her hair "Is that right?" she asked.

"Yes, that'll do. Now comes the ticklish part. Put in water, just a trickle, careful. Now mix it in; add a little more; mix it in—lightly, child, lightly. Never use a heavy hand with pastry. Now divide it into four sections and roll out one piece at a time."

The pastry crumbled so Mary couldn't handle it. She

tried to roll it, but then it stuck fast to the board. She put on flour, but Mrs. Cleaveland warned, "You'll make it hard if you put on too much!"

Finally the bottom crust was laid, patched and ragged, on the pie plate. Mary cut up apples and laid them in neat rows. There were two sugar bowls in the cupboard. Mary took the one with the broken handle and sprinkled its contents on generously. Then she grated nutmeg on the top, as she had seen her mother-in-law do.

The top crust! She rolled it quite smoothly, cut little slits in the fold, and laid it neatly on the pie. With the whalebone jagger knife she fluted the edges.

"Well, now, that looks like a real good pie. I shouldn't know, *hardly*, but what I made it myself." Mary smiled. Mrs. Cleaveland was really quite kind.

The second pie was easier.

Mary put both pies into the oven proudly. She could hardly wait for them to be finished. She kept opening the oven door and looking in.

"Set down, for goodness' sakes!" Mrs. Cleaveland's patience was at an end. "You're buzzing around like a bluebottle."

"Oh, I hope they're good. May I look in now?"

"No."

Mary didn't dare ask again. She sat on the edge of the chair. She was sure she smelled them burning.

"Well, are you going to burn those pies up, now you've got 'em this far?"

Mary jumped up and went to the oven. The pies looked just right, a nice even brown. She tasted a bit of the crust that was loose. "Um—it's good!"

97

"Put them in the buttery and let them be!"

But Mary couldn't help going in once in a while to look at them. She could hardly wait for dinnertime, and then it seemed as though the men would never get through with their corned beef and cabbage so they could have their dessert.

Mary brought in the pie. She cut it. Pieces of apple fell out, but they looked juicy and appetizing. The crust broke up, flaky and tender.

Mrs. Cleaveland noted the interest around the table. She'd no idea Mary would do so well the first time. She herself would have to look to her laurels.

Daniel was the first to take a bite. "Excuse me!" he said.

The men left, one by one. Mary's face fell. Her mother-in-law took a small piece and spit it back into her plate.

"You ninny!" she said. "You've put salt in the apples instead of sugar!"

18

MARY was standing at the kitchen window looking out towards the west across the valley to the churchyard on the opposite hill. She could see it plainly now because the trees were shedding their leaves. Everything was beginning to look bare.

The kitchen was warm and smelled of Indian pudding that her mother-in-law had put in the oven before she had left. It made a comfortable cooking sound, muffled by the oven door.

Mary still wanted to cook, but she hadn't dared to ask again. One afternoon she had experimented, rather doubtfully, but Mrs. Cleaveland came home before she had done more than get out supplies and berated her soundly for attempting to waste good food as she had done before. The salt pie was a sensitive subject to Mary, but no one avoided it. It was discussed among the neighbors.

What could she do this afternoon? She couldn't cook. It seems one didn't cook in the afternoon anyway. There was nothing to do, nowhere to go.

She watched the old captain and Sylvanus and the dog leave for Holmes's Hole. She saw Daniel hitch up to take his mother to the knitting bee at Mrs. Liddy Hancock's. Mary wanted to go, too, but she hadn't been invited. At least Mrs. Cleaveland had not passed on any invitation. Mary sat down, put her elbows on the window sill, and her chin on her hands.

November! The little gardens were blooming in Sydney. Native flowers and posies from old England were nestled in the vacant patches of the city, and the botanical garden was at its best. She dropped her arms on the sill, put her head on them, and cried.

So completely did she give herself up to her loneliness that she didn't hear horse's hoofs and carriage wheels turning in at the gate. She heard the door open and looked up, startled to see Daniel looking down at her.

"Mary," he whispered.

She rose quickly and wiped away the tears, but new ones kept forming. "I'm sorry," she gasped between sobs. "I didn't know anyone was around."

Daniel strode over and put his arm about her. "Don't cry," he said. "Don't."

"I was thinking of—I was lonely, that's all. I thought everyone was gone."

"I went. But I came back again. Ma figured she couldn't get me to stay at Liddy Hancock's while they were knitting mittens, so she had another job ready for me, one that would take me over north. But I thought I might as well take the extra trip home for the sake of having company, maybe. Want to go?"

"Oh, yes! Wait till I put my bonnet on. It won't take a minute." She sped upstairs for her wraps.

Daniel stood there, hat in hand. "Poor Mary!" He thought of that little girl singing at the bow of the *Emma Prescott.* James had no business to bring her here. He ought to have married Saphrony Cathcart. She could have got along all right while James was gone. Her folks were here, and she wouldn't have expected any different from a whaler. She was kind of plain-looking, though, compared with Mary. No, you couldn't blame him. Mary, the little imp, had bewitched him with her winning ways. Godfrey! There was something about her that made *him* tingle all over, too.

Here she was! You'd never know she had been crying, except that her cheeks were flushed.

"Where are we going, Danny?" No one but Mary ever called him that. It sounded nice the way she said it. "I'm glad you came back for me. How blue the sky is! And the air is nice and crisp."

"Going to be warm enough?"

"Oh, yes. This is my heaviest jacket."

"The air comes up cool towards evening. I'll take the warm carriage robe."

Daniel locked the door and put the key on the inside of the blind. Mary ran ahead and jumped lightly into the carriage without waiting for Daniel's hand to help her to a seat. He sat beside her, and they were off, trotting smoothly down the dirt road and down the sandy one to

Scotchman's Bridge, over the little brook, and on to the Lambert's Cove Road.

The horse's hoofs tapped against the dry leaves underfoot. The wheels rustled in them. The brown leaves kept sifting down in the woods, making the air audible in the stillness of the world; and then a little gust would come and shake the leaves down faster, making them whirl round and round ahead of the carriage. "If James were here," thought Mary, "November would be pleasant."

The fields were brown, and where the corn had grown last summer in waving feathery plumes and long, green blades, brown stalks were now piled in neat tepees. Orange pumpkins were being harvested and taken to the barns.

"Begins to look like Thanksgiving!"

"What *is* Thanksgiving?"

"What is Thanksgiving?" Daniel laughed. "Don't you know? You *are* a little heathen!"

"Is it religious?"

"Yes. The governor issues a proclamation, and every year people thank the Lord for bringing them to this country."

"And what do you think of that!" Mary used a touch of the Irish brogue that occasionally crept into her speech.

Daniel looked at her quickly, but he couldn't make out whether she was serious or not. "Mary, you aren't sorry you came?"

"How can I say, Danny, when I'm all alone so much? You and Father are busy with man's affairs. Your mother hates to have me in the house. I can't do anything right."

"Ma's particular sometimes."

"And everything topsy-turvy—leaves falling off the trees getting ready for winter now in November. And I try to be friendly, but no one understands. The girls all laugh at me."

"Ma's probably said something funny about you, told them about your salting the pie or something. You know how she is!" and Daniel laughed at the remembrance of some witty saying of his mother's.

"If James were here. . . . "

"James! James! James!" Daniel was thinking. "He always has everything. A ship and money and a chance to make more—everyone's good will and now this girl he made his wife." He looked down at her, at her dark wavy hair showing under her bonnet where it tilted up like her nose. He remembered the first time he had seen her, singing. He hadn't had a chance then. He hadn't heard her singing lately. He'd found her crying. *He* could make her happy—until James came back. And then? He looked down at her again, at her lips with the little dimple below the corner of her mouth.

"Mary! James isn't here, but I am, and I lo—"

"Danny, Danny, no! Don't spoil everything. Help me sometimes like this afternoon when I feel so desolate, but don't say that!"

She didn't dare to look at him. She looked away at the sky, at the stretch of Vineyard Sound that showed slate-blue between the hills, at the ships. Most of all she looked at the ships. A five-masted schooner was sailing along as though drawn by a string through a miniature lake. There was a brig and a sloop. She knew them all now. One of them might have news.

"Dan, could one of those ships, perhaps, have passed the *Mary Wilder?*"

"No, they're outward bound."

"When can we expect to hear?"

"You're always thinking of James." Daniel sounded petulant.

"Yes, or of my mother in Sydney. It is over a year since I last saw her. I haven't heard from her since."

Her voice was sad. But she had found a subject that it seemed safe to discuss. She told Daniel about her brothers, Mark and Joseph, at home. How she used to play cards with them . . .

"You play cards!"

"Yes. I used to play by the hour, and I hate cards! But I used to play to keep them from the grogshops."

"Did they drink?"

"Yes, when they had lots of money in their pockets and were feeling good, or when they had none at all and were feeling low. Other times I could hold them, and Pa, too. We'd play cards all the evening or else we'd sing. There were some jolly songs they learned from the sailors, and they'd teach them to me. I'd sing the verse part, and they'd sing the chorus." She held her head back and sang:

> *As I was a-walkin' down Paradise Street,*
> *To me aye, aye—blow the man down!*
> *A saucy young p'liceman I chanced for to meet;*
> *Blow the man down to me aye, aye, blow the man down!*

Whether he's white man or black man or brown,
Give me some time to blow the man down,
Give me some time to blow the man down,
Blow the man down! bullies!

David joined in the chorus,

Aye, aye, blow the man down!

The woods rang with it. A little squirrel dropped his hazelnut and scurried up a tree. The horse trotted along evenly. He had heard sea chanties before.

"We're most there, now."

"Shall I wait here? I'll hold the reins."

"All right. I won't be gone long."

Mary sat there listening to the leaves rustling against each other, to the caw of an occasional crow, to the note of the chickadee that came to peek at her inquisitively. The air smelled like apples and warm barns. Underlying all the sensations of the November countryside was the thought of Danny, wanting her.

How easy it would be to be swept into the rapids of passion with Daniel's arms about her, with his mocking, jaunty voice whispering his careless love, with his lips . . . Her body, that James had made her aware of, quivered at the thought. But she was James's wife! She didn't want to be awakened to the joys of other arms. She would not move close to Daniel as she should have done the week before if they had been driving where stretches of west wind caught them. She would sit on her own end of the carriage seat, talking lightly all the way home through the dusky woods, talking flippantly to keep deeper moods from coming to the surface.

19

IT WAS late when they reached home. Mrs. Cleaveland had driven back with one of the neighbors, and she was busy getting supper with her silk dress rustling ominously under an apron.

"Where's Mary?"

"I dunno, Ma. There was nobody here when we come back," Sylvanus answered.

"What! Did she go off somewhere and leave the door unlocked?"

"No. 'Twas locked. We found the key in the regular place."

"I didn't know she knew the place."

"She knows a good deal," the old captain said in a friendly way.

"You're right, she does!" But this was said in a different manner. "Not grape jelly, Addie, the quince. Go right down cellar again and get the quince."

"Eliza, do you know where Mary is?"

"No, Ma. I haven't seen her since I came back from school."

"Like enough she's at the post office," Sylvanus volunteered, and they all laughed. All but Mrs. Cleaveland.

"Here's Dan'l, I guess. Sounds like our horse and carriage. Where's he been?"

"Over north. I sent him over to Wade Norton's of an errand. I don't like to leave him here in the house. I don't like the way he looks at Mary."

"He won't hurt her." Captain Cleaveland tried to reassure her.

"Law! She'll hurt him! That's what worries me."

The door opened, and Mary and Daniel came in, bringing a whiff of fresh air and the smell of harness leather.

"Well, what's the meaning of this?"

There didn't seem to be anything to say in answer. The silence seemed to infuriate Mrs. Cleaveland. "Mary," she demanded, "Don't you realize you're a married woman?"

"Yes, indeed. I shouldn't have driven out unchaperoned, otherwise."

Mrs. Cleaveland was somewhat taken aback, but not for long. She shook the long-handled spoon. "You're a huzzy! That's what you are, a huzzy, or you wouldn't try to lead my boys astray."

The color mounted higher in Mary's cheeks. She bit her lip, then answered with dignity, "Your boys can take care of themselves, Mrs. Cleaveland."

Daniel was beginning to enjoy the situation. He had

107

dreaded it at first. Now he saw his older brother Sylvanus looking at him with curiosity and a new admiration. He saw that his mother had forgotten his part in the affair, asking Mary to go with him. He knew it was useless to put in a word for Mary, so he kept perfectly still.

Mary looked to him for help but saw that it could not be expected. She looked at Sylvanus. She could see in his eyes that he believed her capable of anything. He was not like James with his firm New England conscience that the world had been unable to touch, or like Danny with his young wonderings. She felt as if she were standing naked before his mocking eyes. She drew her arms closer to her body and ran from them all. Even James's father had said nothing in her behalf. He had been sitting there, absently turning the pages of the almanac.

In her room Mary could hear the west wind rattling the window sash. She paced up and down, trying to ignore it and trying not to notice the pounding of her heart.

It had been so nice to have Dan come and take her out when she was lonely! It had been so nice to feel again that she was wanted.

And now, though she had been virtuous and had turned aside all advances, the friendly relations between Danny and herself had the imprint of this woman's suspicions. They could never be the same.

Even Father—and that was the hardest to bear—even Father believed her guilty.

She might as well have taken all she could get of affection. It was little enough! Then she was quickly ashamed of the thought. No, she was James's wife, and it was James she loved.

The wind blew a gusty breath, and dead leaves rattled in circles against the frozen ground. What was that? A knock against the door?

It was repeated.

"Who's there?"

"Father."

Mary opened the door gladly. She felt like rushing into his arms, she was so relieved—when she saw that he had a tray. He'd brought her some Indian pudding, cold now, and some biscuits and jelly.

"Oh!" It was not food she wanted, but it did smell good.

Captain Cleaveland set it down on a chair.

"Father," Mary asked hesitatingly, looking into his eyes, "Father, you don't believe. . . ?"

"No, no, child! Nobody does. Just reef your tops'ls, Mary, and wait till the gale blows over."

20

THE friendship between Mary and Eliza grew more intimate. Eliza would come and sit on Mary's bed each night and tell her of the day's activities at school.

"Let me brush your hair, Eliza. It is so pretty with reddy-gold lights in it, and it's so thick and wavy. You are growing more beautiful each day."

Then Eliza told her about Ezra Cottle, how he whistled a certain tune for her as he went by the school-house. "I always blush. I just can't help it." And how Ezra sometimes waited for her at the steps of the store and walked home with her.

"I wondered why you were always so eager to do errands. You used not to like the long walk over the brook. And you take so long to return!"

"Don't tell Ma. She wouldn't like it."

"Why not, Eliza? There's nothing more natural in the

world, my mother always said, than for a nice boy and nice girl to be together, just so long as they have an older person at hand. I'll stay with you any time."

So Eliza did bring him home one evening, and Mrs. Cleaveland accepted him quite naturally. Yes, her daughter was growing up. She brought out cookies and doughnuts and went back into the kitchen. Mary got out her embroidery and sat down in the front room with the young couple.

A nice chap, he was! They all talked together, Ezra sitting on the sofa beside Eliza, and Mary on the other side of the room, not noticing, apparently, that they held each other's hands beneath the wide folds of Eliza's dress.

Everything was pleasant until Mrs. Cleaveland appeared in the doorway and beckoned to Mary. She carefully shut the door and led Mary to the kitchen. "You stay here," she commanded. "I'll not have you trying to take Eliza's beau away from her."

The house seemed very quiet. Mrs. Cleaveland was out taking her turn at caring for old Mrs. Becky Vincent. She had taken her a custard, and she would sit and talk to her until someone else came in to relieve her.

Mary was trying to read one of the thick leather-bound volumes that old Captain Cleaveland kept in the front room, but the day was dull and the print small on the yellowing paper. Mary never cared much for reading anyway. She preferred company and gaiety. She was glad when Daniel came in with a pack of cards.

"Come on, Mary," he said. "Teach us to play cards."

"Don't you know how?" asked Mary, surprised.

"You teach us. Then we'll know. Teach us that game they call whist."

"We'd have to have four to play whist."

"Well, there's Sylvanus and me, and Ezra's out by the barn."

"All right, if they want to play."

So Daniel rounded up the boys while Mary cleared the small table by removing the curios to the mantel and folding up the cloth. She had thought she never wanted to see another card as long as she lived. But now she was humming as she dusted off the table. She was thinking, with a pang of homesickness, that she'd like to play another game with her father and Mark and Joseph, playing with every nerve on the game so those quick Irish minds would be kept alert and their imaginations not allowed to wander to the false glories of lower McKesson Street.

Daniel threw the cards down on the table, a well-worn pack. The boys sat around and watched Mary deal. Her hands moved gracefully in a steady rhythm.

"Take up your cards, and sort them into suits, all the diamonds together, all the hearts and clubs and spades."

But it was not long before Mary realized that the Cleaveland boys knew how to play cards as well as she did, as well as her brothers, even. Only Ezra was fumbling with his cards, unused to them. They all helped him.

"You know how to play!"

"We couldn't live this long where we been without knowing a heart from a spade. Pa doesn't allow cards on shipboard, but he can't forbid 'em along the waterfront of Frisco."

For a moment Mary was aghast. "Father doesn't allow you to play cards?" she asked incredulously. She didn't want to do anything of which Father would disapprove.

"He don't like cards on shipboard," Sylvanus explained. "It leads the men to gambling and brawling and wasting time. And he wouldn't have the officers do a thing he had forbid the men."

"We'll put them away," said Mary firmly.

"Oh, Mary!" they exclaimed, ruefully. "We haven't had a good game in over a year, and Ezra was just beginning to get the notion!"

"Yes, hold on! I'd just got so's the cards would spread out nice without falling."

"Come on, Sylvanus. Give them to me." She was in earnest now. She had all the cards in her hand when Mary Ann Cleaveland walked in, followed by Eliza.

"What did I tell you?" Mary Ann announced dramatically. "A low-living, cardplaying huzzy! There, Eliza. She's got your brothers and your young man, and she's teaching 'em to gamble."

"We knew how before, Ma!" Sylvanus admitted, but Mrs. Cleaveland would not listen.

"We were just putting them away. As soon as we. . . ." Mary stopped. She didn't want to get the boys in trouble. They knew cardplaying was not permitted.

"As soon as you heard us coming, I dare say!"

It was no use to protest. Sylvanus started to, but Mary put her hand on his sleeve. She realized it would be useless for the boys to say anything in her behalf. She'd go and tell Father. He'd understand. But he'd blame his sons. Well, they should be blamed. They knew the rules. She'd go and tell him before his wife did. But the more she thought the less she liked the idea. If Father believed her and made allowances, as no doubt he would, he'd try to put in a good word for her, and then his life would be miserable. No, she would bear the blame herself.

But Eliza! Mary didn't like the way Eliza looked at her. As soon as she'd seen Ezra playing cards with Mary she had blushed with hot color. "I was waiting for you, Ezra, down by the brook."

21

MARY was thrown back more and more on her own resources. She had turned against herself Mrs. Cleaveland's one friendly act by putting salt in the pies. Never again, Mary knew, would her mother-in-law allow her to do any cooking.

Father, she felt, hadn't liked her cardplaying, though she found out later that Sylvanus and Daniel had confessed that they had started the game and that Mary had refused to go on with it as soon as she had heard that he disapproved.

And Daniel, who had been her friend—she must keep Daniel at arm's length. Sylvanus she had never trusted. Eliza was now very cool to her, and Mrs. Cleaveland never lost an opportunity of widening the breach by pointing out that Ezra looked at Mary with a great deal of interest. Addie was too young to be much company, and anyway Mary scorned to make a companion of her after Eliza had become unfriendly. She'd go her own way and meet people in the village.

Before she went out in the afternoon Mary tried to do a reasonable share of the housework, but that was difficult, for Mary Ann insisted that no one could do it right. Even Eliza and Addie had few privileges in the kitchen. Mary tidied up the front part of the house each morning, and each afternoon if she stayed long enough she would see Mrs. Cleaveland going around rearranging things or pretending to hunt for articles that were mislaid when Mary "switched that broom around."

At noon, right after dinner, she'd do the dishes. Mrs. Cleaveland usually went over them with a cloth before she put them on the table, to indicate that Mary had made a slipshod job of it.

Mary began to call on Susan Vincent or Mary Manter or Nancy Allen in the afternoons. They received her with formality at first. They liked her, but they stood rather in awe of the family and were afraid of what the elder Mrs. Cleaveland could do with her tongue. So more often Mary walked down the mill road to the place where the new church was being built. She liked the smell of new lumber. She liked to watch the workmen fit together the big timbers and smooth down the planks with a heavy plane that made the wood shine yellow under the iron blade and turn out above it like curls of sunny hair.

It was there that she found old Tim McNeill, who talked with an Irish flavor that reminded Mary of her father. He'd been a carpenter on shipboard, he told her. About two o'clock in the afternoon he'd start to look for her, and then he'd bustle about, whistling as he turned over plank after plank to get the right one for a certain jointure. Moses Vincent liked to see her, too, for Tim was a contentious old man and would turn surly and morose if he wasn't catered to. But let him catch sight of young Mrs. Cleaveland coming down the road, and he'd brighten right up and go to work with vigor.

She'd greet them all, then turn to Tim. "And would you look at that!" She unconsciously spoke with the rolling tone she had used when talking intimately with her father. "Like a piece of embroidery it is, to be sure, where the joints match and the ends fit together." They couldn't talk much above the hammering and sawing, but the old man liked to see her there. He liked her praise and the inspiration of her presence.

"What kind of church is this?" she asked, during a pause in his work.

"Bapthist, they say. It's all one an' the same to me."

"It's not the same kind as the one over the brook?"

"No, there's a shlight differince. Here they believe you'll go to hell if you ain't had a duckin' in Uncle Sith's Pond, and in the ither they believe you will if you do. It's the same as the Bapthist Church over to Middletown."

"Was it so crowded they needed another?"

"Bah!" He made a wry face. "'Twas the contrariness of human nature, to be sure." And he told her about the flatiron feud. How one woman had accused another of stealing her flatiron, and it had broken up the membership into two distinct groups.

"And they raised money enough to build another church?"

"Is it true you haven't heard?" Tim looked at her inquiringly.

"Just enough to make me curious. Tell me."

Then he took the nails from his mouth and told her about it between hammering and sawing with a touch of awe in his voice. For all his professions of disbelief, he was, like Mary, still Irish.

The Baptists "to the east'ard" had felt the need of a church and they had met at the homes of different members and prayed for guidance. "And would you believe it," Tim lowered his voice until Mary had to lean forward to hear him, "there was such a run of fish in Deep Bottom Cove, to be sure, you'd thought Jesus had multiplied 'em like the loaves and the fishes on the mount. The mimbers sold enough fish to put up this meetin' house, to pay me me wages, and more."

Yes, Mary had heard the story, but she had begun to realize by this time that the stories the Cleavelands told were colored by their prejudices, and they had no use for the Baptists.

The Cleavelands had no use for Baptists or Methodists. Originally there had been only one church in the village, and that one, as Mrs. Cleaveland said, run as a church should be, by the votes of the congregation and with normal religious experiences. There was no bowing or scraping, no ducking in Uncle Seth's pond, not any ranting and hollering. They used to tell some remarkable stories of the Methodist prayer meetings held at the Cathcart Tavern, when Asa Norton jumped up to swing from the rafters, shouting "Hallelujah!" One of the Cleavelands usually went on purpose to make fun of it.

With most of the villagers Catholicism had never been a problem, for there was no Catholic church on the Island. They thought nothing of it, except to consider it vaguely as some ritualistic religion. Mrs. Cleaveland, however, disapproved of "popery" and looked on Mary as a fit subject for missionary work. She thought it was her duty to bring Mary into the fold.

Each Sunday she took her to church with the rest of the family, as regularly as the day came around.

She regretted the empty pews. "When I was a girl," she'd say, "there wasn't a soul in the village that didn't come to church here and pay his share of the upkeep, too, or they'd know the reason why." Yes, everything had been all right until the Baptists left to build a church of their own over on Scotchman's Road. "And now they're building another one. Well, 'twon't last. They'll set to fightin'," she concluded.

So Mary went with the family to the Congregational meetinghouse each Lord's Day.

22

How different was this little white building from the church of her childhood! They could see it just across the valley as they walked around the pond, across the stream near the mill, and up the rise past Mr. Whiting's house. There was the church, plain and austere, standing in "God's Acre." Every stone in the little cemetery, from the gray, lichened one of Simon Athearn to the little white marble of James's infant sister, was known to the members of the congregation.

She had been used to entering another world on Sunday. At home in Sydney they would dress up in their poor best and go to Saint Patrick's on Church Hill. It was a beautiful building, made of stone, decorated with statues and ornaments, and surmounted with a cross. Inside you felt your troubles submerged by the grandeur and religious atmosphere. She enjoyed the early morning light shining through the stained-glass windows, the odor of incense, and best of all the lovely singing. Mary had always looked forward to Sunday.

This morning when she entered the church the air was chill except in the pews next to the stove. She wondered if she had sinned during the week, for if she had, the God of this Church would be inexorable.

Captain Cleaveland ushered them in, first his wife, then Mary, then the girls. They had barely seated themselves when Mr. Cole mounted the pulpit steps and looked with dignity upon his flock. At a signal the melodeon rolled out "Old Hundred." The congregation rose and each singer vied with this neighbor in singing:

From all that dwell below the skies,
Let the Creator's name arise:
Let the Redeemer's name be sung,
Through every land, by every tongue.

The people remained standing for the prayer, rigid in their places, with heads high.

Mary always wanted to kneel, but she tried to do as the others did. Once when she bowed involuntarily at the name of Christ, Mrs. Cleaveland nudged her. "No popery!" she whispered so loudly that Deacon Allen turned around to stare at Mary.

During Mr. Cole's long sermons she found herself getting tired and inattentive. She began to notice the people around her. In the wing pews sat the deacons, looking solemn, as the occasion demanded. Deacon Cottle sat there with his kind, friendly face, but the other deacon looked as though he had eaten sour apples. The

Cleaveland pew was near the front, the Allens back of them, and the minister's pew beside them.

When the congregation finally arose for the closing hymn, Mary sang eagerly. As they were leaving, Deacon Cottle came to her. "I could hear your singing, child," he said, "above all the others." Her face flushed with pleasure.

Poor little girl! He didn't believe she had a very happy time, everything strange and new, her husband away, and no friends here. "I should admire to have you come over and spend the day with us. I'll call for you the day after tomorrow." Mary could hardly speak, she was so grateful. She left the church with a lighthearted little skip.

Mrs. Cleaveland turned to a neighbor with a significant nod toward Mary. "I don't have to send my money *away* to the heathen."

23

MARY had been out in the barn for a long time, standing close beside Hunter, scratching his nose, and
leaning her head against his smooth, warm neck. She had
been standing there against his shoulder, crying.

Suddenly she straightened, "Oh, Hunter, I must stop
this foolishness. He'll come back, and then—and then—
and then—" Her voice rose into a little song.

The horse turned around and rubbed his head against
her sleeve.

"How about some oats, boy? Would you like some?"
Mary went to the grain room, took a handful of oats
from the bin, and held them out in her palm. She liked
the touch of the horse's velvety nose against her hand.

"There, now!" She gave the horse a friendly slap.
"I'll help John feed the hens and see if there are any
eggs. . . . John," she called, "I'll feed the hens."

"All right, Mis' James. Yo' know, Ah b'lieves the hens

lays betta fo' yo' than fo' me. Las' time yo' gathered up the aigs, they was most a dozen. When Ah get 'em they ain't mor'n ten or 'leben." He chuckled happily.

Mary took a measure of grain and called, "Here, chick, chick, chick." She liked to see them run, eagerly, comically. She threw the corn far into the yard and watched them flutter and scramble, picking each other's necks and combs.

Then she unlatched the gate, looked in all the nests, and counted the eggs as she put them into the wooden measure—eleven, twelve, thirteen. "Thirteen, John!"

"Oh, Mis' James, dat's bad luck!" But still he chuckled.

As she went into the house, she called, "Guess how many eggs, Mother Cleaveland?"

There was no answer. And then she saw that her mother-in-law had company. The door was open into the parlor, where three women sat in stiff correctness on the horsehair chairs.

"I'm sorry!" Mary stammered, but Mrs. Cathcart smiled indulgently and said, "I don't believe Saphrony has met James's wife."

"Come in, Mary," Mrs. Cleaveland called, hoping that Mary would refuse.

Mary put down the measure of eggs in the kitchen, poured water from the well bucket over her hands, and dried them quickly. Then she smoothed her dress and went in.

"How do you do, dear," Mrs. Cathcart said sweetly. "You've never met my daughter, Saphronia. 'Phrony, dear, this is Mrs. James Cleaveland."

1 2 4

Mary came forward. She had been taught to be as gracious in calico as in silk, if there was no way out of the one into the other. She was ready to curtsy and hold out her hand, but this other young woman merely nodded coolly and sat there looking her over. The room was very quiet.

Mary felt the pity one feels for well-meaning but ill-mannered people, and then she looked at Saphrony's eyes—aloof and calculating. A strange cold feeling went over Mary. It was as though this girl hated her. "How ridiculous!" Mary tried to persuade herself. "Why should she?"

Before she had a chance to get another impression, Mrs. Cleaveland arose. "Whew, Mary! What a smell of the stables you're flourishing around here! We'd better open the window."

"I'm sorry, Mrs. Cleaveland. I'll leave."

As Mary went upstairs she heard her mother-in-law fussing with the window catch. She heard Mrs. Hannah Johnson say, "Mary Ann, it ain't right the way you treat that child." Sitting by the window overhead, she couldn't help hearing Mrs. Cleaveland turn on her guest. "She didn't have to come here if she wasn't prepared to accept our ways."

"Maybe James forced her to come." This was the voice of Saphronia Cathcart, in bright, sarcastic tone, followed by laughter rippling down the scale. Mary didn't like that laugh.

Mrs. Cathcart spoke indulgently, "Isn't Saphrony just too funny!"

But Hannah Johnson, unafraid, was not to be turned

aside. "She has a right to expect common decency, and I'm ashamed of you, Mary Ann."

Mrs. Johnson left. Mary could feel the house tremble under her indignant tread.

Mary smiled a little wistfully; there was a friend.

But who was this Saphronia Cathcart? Where had she been all summer? Why hadn't she seen her before? And why should she feel tension in the air between them at the first meeting?

24

MARY was walking as fast as she could through the bare, wet woods. The snow that still lay thick among the trees was melting in the afternoon sun. She picked her footing almost unconsciously, for she was too engrossed in her thoughts to notice where she trod. She was not aware of the bright February sun. She was deaf to the little birds that flew ahead of her a bit and then stopped to chatter beside her, "Chick-a-dee, chick-a-dee-dee-dee." She didn't even know that Pilot was following with his tail between his legs and his head bowed. It seemed as though he knew he had brought trouble to Mary.

She was going to Deacon Cottle's. His home had been a haven to her many times since that first visit. The deacon and his wife and their large family had taken her in as one of them and loved her. She would never forget their kindness.

She thought of the first time she had ever been there, when each child had put himself out to entertain her. She had sat down on the floor with them and played at their games, told them stories of the beauties of Hawaii or of Sydney. She had told them of her father and mother, of her brothers, and of the little kangaroo that Joseph had captured. She never talked about these things at Mrs. Cleaveland's.

Deacon Cottle had watched her as she played. "Why, you're nothing but a little girl yourself," he'd said kindly.

Mary thought of the many times since then when he had come to fetch her when he had been in the village for supplies. She'd go at a moment's notice, for she was sure of a cordial welcome to their home and to their simple meals.

"Look here, Abbie, we've got company."

Mrs. Cottle would wipe her hands on her apron and take off her spectacles, for she used to study poetry with a book propped before her while she washed the clothes or dried the dishes. There was so much work to be done in a large family, with keeping the children clean and educating them. But Mary's coming never made any difference.

"Why, Mary! I'm glad to see you." And at meal times, "I've got a great kettle of hulled corn heating on the coals and plenty of milk for dinner," or "We'll dip into that pot of hasty pudding."

Little Belle would set an extra bowl on the big, well-scrubbed table, and a pitcher of fresh milk. Mrs. Cottle served the food, steaming and fragrant, and the deacon said a blessing with as much dignity as though their simple meal had been a banquet. They talked on topics of the times, both sides of the slavery issue, of town affairs, of the prose and poetry of the ages. If Eliot and William had a difference of opinion that waxed too violent, Deacon Cottle quoted the passage, "Better is a dinner of herbs, where love is, than a stalled ox and hatred therewith."

"Yes," thought Mary. "How much more enjoyable this dish of hulled corn and milk than those bountiful meals at the Cleavelands' where silence sometimes veils hatred."

That was where she was going—to the Cottles'. She wouldn't tell them why she'd come. She'd be ashamed to. But she'd feel better for their kindness and their love.

She was more than halfway there. Somewhere near here there was a short cut across the field. It must be just the other side of the woods. As she hesitated, planning the way, the sun picked out a bright red boxberry among the leaves that were poking their way through round holes in the melting snow. She stooped to pick it with its reddish-green leaves. She'd take it to little Belle. "Is it the thin coating of snow or the wet earth that makes it smell so sweet?"

Something moved behind her. She was startled, "Why, Pilot!"

Pilot came closer, crouching down, dragging his hind legs after him in the muddy road, wagging his tail.

"Pilot, such sorrow you cause me, to be sure," she said sadly.

The dog licked his chops shamefacedly and flopped down at her feet. She patted his head, and then the whole horrid scene came before her eyes again.

Pilot had looked in vain in the kitchen, in the woodshed, and in the barnyard. He finally pattered up the back stairs, scratched open her door, and at last found Mary, lying face down on her bed.

He jumped up on her, nuzzled her bent head, licked her face, and, after restoring her to cheerfulness, climbed down to take a nap under the bed.

But as Mary looked up, she saw that Pilot had been out in the barnyard where the snow had been trampled and churned until it was a slushy muck, and that the coverlet was streaked with mud.

"Pilot, you bad dog!" she reprimanded, then picked up a cloth and tried to brush away the dirt, but before she made much progress, she looked up to see Mrs. Cleaveland standing in the doorway, staring at the grimy imprint on the spread, on *her* good bedspread. The older woman's wrath was mounting high. When she saw Pilot, her husband's dog, looking guiltily from beneath the bed, her anger reached its peak. Mary braced as she had done on shipboard, waiting for the shock of a heavy sea. It came, rolling around her in a flood of bitter words, wave after wave of heated feeling, a backwash of disappointment that her son James should have "sunk so low as to marry a dirty little Papist."

Mary was left speechless with the attack, but was ready for action. She had put on her outdoor clothes, and now she was walking blindly across the fields, over stone walls, by muddy roads, and through the woods.

"Come on, Pilot. It's not your fault. 'Twould have been something else."

Being restored to the good graces he had thought himself deprived of, Pilot jumped up and ran to chase birds and squirrels, panting happily.

But Mary couldn't help thinking about the whole situation, and she walked faster and faster across the slushy fields.

There were so many times when she had fled to her own room. When she decided she must go downstairs and try to be folks, Mrs. Cleaveland would perhaps command Eliza to throw open the windows. When there was company she'd forget to pass Mary the tea. In her own room Mary could at least get under the covers and cry.

The snow lay smoothly on the hill ahead with grass and weedstalks peeping through, and over the brow of it she could see a wisp of smoke rising—smoke from the Cottle hearth.

She hurried, running the last few yards. She knocked at the door.

"Come in!" Mrs. Cottle was working on a rag mat, sewing the braids firmly together. "Why, child!" she exclaimed. Then seeing her troubled face she held out her arms to Mary.

And Mary bowed her head on Mrs. Cottle's shoulder and cried and cried and cried.

25

THERE was more snow that spring, but the days began to grow longer. In the noonday sun the snow melted quickly, and icicles that formed at night snapped and fell from the eaves each morning with a thud and tinkle like breaking glass. The field across the road showed bare in spots. The twigs no longer looked hard and brittle, but from a distance they seemed to have a delicate sheen of life.

Toward night the sun still set red and cold behind the hills. Drops of water would collect from the roof, running more and more slowly till they lost all power to reach the earth and grew like rapiers, pendant. The evening star shone bright in the west, and the new moon was a thin line of silver.

Mary put on her knitted hood and cape to go out. She felt the ground, frosted slightly, stretching like India rubber under her feet. She could smell the spring, and

132

hark! Pinkletinks! The sound that James had loved, little Vineyard frogs piping hopefully in the swamps.

Soon there were only a few stubborn patches of snow left on the hills. It seemed as though they would never go, but finally the Mayflowers came, and she shared with the New England girls the joy of finding the first one. Mary hadn't known what to look for, but she was always ready for an outdoor trip. She walked along with Eliza and Adeline Cleaveland and two or three other girls from the village, each with a basket. Suddenly at her feet she saw a pale, delicate blossom, almost hidden in the bright green moss and dried leaves. She leaned down, calling, "Look, look!" She had never seen anything more beautiful. The little pink Christmas flowers of Australia never had the subtlety of this. Was it the cold, hard winter that made this dainty flower seem so desirable, or was it some essence of the flower itself? The other girls scattered through the woods. They were scraping away the old oak leaves and pulling up great handfuls—like primitive virgins, drunk with the coming of spring— while she, still on her knees, admired one little bloom.

Then came May! The lilacs and apple blossoms were just as beautiful as they were last year when she had first seen them. She was eighteen now, though she felt much older. That year had been an eternity.

In May a packet of letters came from Paita, addressed to the captain's mother. Mrs. Cleaveland looked over the letters. There was one to Mrs. Caroline Athearn in the childish hand of Edwin Williams Athearn. He was twelve years old, though the crew list must have said fifteen. The authorities were getting particular about ships taking young boys nowadays. Well, James would be good to him. He'd be better off than he was at home. Poor Mrs. Athearn had nothing much to do with. There was a letter for Mrs. Norton from Mayhew, cooper on the *Mary Wilder*. That family could always do anything. Richard Thompson would take that over north when he went to see his girl. Yes, there was one addressed to Mary. Mrs. Cleaveland handed it over reluctantly. There was none for her.

Mary seized it. She felt like dancing around and around the kitchen floor. She did essay a few steps in spite of the hostile eyes upon her. Eliza and Addie, sharing her high spirits, took her arm and executed a few maneuvers. Finally Mary ran out in the sun on the east step to read it.

"Australian bushwhacker!" muttered Mrs. Cleaveland.

In a few minutes Mary came in with the letter. She knew it was for all of them as well as for her. It was a friendly, newsy letter. In each sentence she could see something personal, yet she could read it aloud without a blush. He had 240 barrels of sperm. She asked her mother-in-law how many whales that would be, but Mrs. Cleaveland pretended to be busy and not interested in Mary's letter. The girls figured about sixty or eighty barrels to a whale. That would be about four whales. That was good for so early in the season; it was only March when he wrote. They'd had one accident. Martin Johnson, a seaman from Norway, had been lost overboard. Swept right off the rigging in a storm. Mary could just feel how the *Mary Wilder* had pitched and tossed in that sea. She felt her stomach turn at the thought of it and at the thought of that living body plunged down into the sea, never to be seen again. All the same, she wished she'd been with James.

He mentioned the different ships he had spoken, with the count of their oil. The captains had asked for news from home. She must send their names to the *Gazette*, so everyone would know the latest reports from those ships. There was a long list of them each week in the shipping news.

He touched lightly on plans for buying a house when he returned. He knew just the house he wanted. Mary did, too. She knew and she wouldn't oppose it, though she thought it was larger than necessary. But some day they might need more room.

Mary read the letter again. She slept with it under her pillow. It got crumpled and worn and frayed. She knew it by heart and could even recite the tally of oil stowed down by the different ships.

June! Roses bloomed against the garden fences; wild rose and elderberry by the roadside. Grapevines blossomed in fragrant tangles. Scythes swung rhythmically in the thick, deep grass, filling the air with the scent of newly cut stalks. Time went more quickly now.

As soon as the weather grew warm they held grove meetings. Down the lane toward Tiah's Cove there was a beautiful grove of spreading oak trees, carpeted with moss underneath, where rude benches had been set. In the pleasant summer evenings the whole community forgot their differences of creed and worshiped God together. Sometimes the Reverend Jesse Pease of Baptist faith led the meeting; at other times, Mr. Cole of the Congregational Church. It was light, ephemeral worship, too druidical for some of the older members; too joyous to be good in the eyes of others. In reality it was real Puritan religion modified by the grandeur of the trees and the canopy of the sky, accompanied by the gentle rustling of the leaves and the distant hum of the surf on the South Side, unhampered by the pompous conceit engendered by man-made meetinghouses.

Children came with lips and fingers ruddy from the sweet wild strawberries that grew along the bank nearby. Sweethearts sat close with feigned indifference. Mary longed for James. She wanted her brothers and sisters. It seemed as though she were the only one among them who was alone.

In July Betsy Luce asked Mary to go huckleberrying with her. They went out on the plains among the scrub oaks, dressed in their oldest clothes, with sunbonnets and big baskets. Betsy had already marked a bush with a piece of her torn calico dress to show them where the berries grew thickest, for Betsy knew all the tricks of finding things in the woods. She liked to acquire things and would dry great crocks of fruit to use for pies next winter. They soon filled their baskets; then Betsy's eyes darted from a near-by, thickly covered bush to one more remote and left reluctantly, for the sun was still high and there were more berries to be had for the picking.

"Don't tell anybody where you've been," Betsy warned.

"I should never be able to find the place if I wanted to."

"I thought not, or I shouldn't have brought you," Betsy frankly admitted.

They trudged back through little wood roads, sweet smelling in the hot sun, which led them to the cool, tall shade behind Mrs. Mary Ann Norton's, in sight of the new church.

"They're going to have singing school in the new Baptist meeting house next winter," said Betsy proudly. "Wouldn't you like to go?"

"Oh, I should admire to, ever so much," answered Mary, and looked forward to it all the rest of the year.

MRS. CLEAVELAND looked with disfavor on Mary's going to singing school in the Baptist meeting-house, but Mary was determined not to be deprived of that. She took a lantern from the woodshed, a few precious matches, and sallied forth. Daniel went with her. Mary teased him about hoping to see Julia Nickerson there.

Betsy Luce joined them. All the young men and girls of the village were there and many of the oldest in-habitants who were still young at heart. Mr. Alphonso Luce stood up. He rapped the front pew for silence, set the pitch with a tuning fork, beat time tentatively, then led off with the old hymns. Later he added some frivo-lous tunes, such as "My Bonnie Lies over the Ocean," "Barbara Allen," "Annie Laurie," "Robin Adair."

Mary had forgotten where she was. Her lovely voice sounded clear above the others, first with resonant pathos in its tone, then with a gay lilt. The others stopped to listen, but Mary kept on alone, till suddenly she realized that she was the center of attention and all were listening to her. She kept on until she got to the chorus, when she turned around and said, "Now, everybody," and they all joined in heartily. From that moment Mary was a leader among the young people.

After another hour they blew out their lamps, lighted candles in the lanterns, stepped out into the chilly night, where the ocean moaned. Mr. Luce closed the door firmly; then they walked along together singing until they came to the corner by the post office, where they parted to go their different ways.

Daniel went on with Julia, so Mary alone turned in at the gate with a sinking heart, for the house looked dark and forbidding. She went as usual to the kitchen door. It would not open. She went around to the back of the house to the east door, which was seldom locked, but this time it resisted. She went to the front door. That, of course, was shuttered tight. Back to the kitchen door she went and stood before it. The feeling of dismay had left her and the feeling of dread. The fear of her mother-in-law's superiority had vanished. In its place was a mounting anger, rising against all the indignities to which she had been subjected. She picked up a stone. This was her home now. She should enter. Suddenly she thought of a better plan. She put the stone down, blew out the lantern and put it carefully beside the door with the few matches she had taken, and, daintily picking up her skirts, she went back along the dark road.

There was a light that shone through the window of

Caroline Luce's into the wintry night. The firelight wavered from the big open hearth. Mary knocked and heard someone move about within in response. Caroline, stout and hearty, pressed her nose against the windowpane.

"Why, Mrs. James Cleaveland, what you doin' here?" Everything had been all right when they had parted a half hour ago. "What's the matter?" she asked in alarm.

"May I stay with you?" Mary faltered. "May I stay—until James comes home?"

"Why, come right in, child. Come right in. Stay as long as you like, and welcome."

Caroline took Mary's cold hands in hers, then swung the iron crane over the fire to make her a cup of tea. The cat left his place by the hearth and came over to rub his warm back in welcome against Mary's ankles. The kettle began to hum, overlaying the dull murmur of the sea. Caroline put hot coals from the fire into the warming pan so that little Mrs. James Cleaveland might sleep in a warm feather bed.

27

THERE followed an interlude of peaceful, rustic life. Each of the two women gave much to the other. Caroline blossomed under the unaccustomed admiration for her abilities, for she had come to the island "from off" to work in the factory, where Theodor, passing daily and newly suffering the loss of his former helpmate, had been captivated by her bulk and capability and ready response to his wit. He had soon come to accept her virtues as his due and to make light of her faults. Her stepdaughters, Martha Ann and Ada, saw her only as an interloper and soon left home in dudgeon. Surely, they thought, they could have looked after the house. Willard Luce, Caroline's father-in-law, was a nice old man, bright and full of witty sayings, but querulous now. He had been postmaster for twenty years, and it hurt his pride that he was no longer considered able. William Mayhew came in daily to attend to the mail.

Old Mr. Luce was secretly amused to think of the new situation in his household. "James Cleaveland's wife living with the Luces! I wonder what that spitfire, Mary Ann, thinks of that?" And one had only to look at Mrs. Henry Cleaveland's face and see the droop to the corners of her mouth to suspect that she didn't relish the change.

When Mary Ann's mother had given up her widowhood to marry Willard Luce, years before, there had been protests. It didn't matter that her mother was happy until she died. Mary Ann could never accept Mr. Luce as her stepfather. She remarked caustically about his inability to supply a fitting stone for her mother's grave, and when she purchased the stone herself had inscribed on it, "Mrs. Mary L., daughter of Hon. George Athearn," without a mention of the husband, only that impersonal initial L.

"What'll be the odds in a hundred years?" said old Willard Luce as he put a bunch of spring flowers on his wife's grave and looked at the insult carved in the stone.

Yes, it was amusing to have the wife of Mary Ann's son James come to his home for refuge.

But old Willard Luce's wit had been perverted in his son Theodor, a perpetrator of practical jokes. Mary would find herself tied to a chair by the apron strings while she was busy peeling potatoes or while her hands were in the dough and the oven ready for a pie. As she moved about the kitchen, a sudden twitch would untie the neat bow and Mary would find herself without an apron entirely. Mary's response to such levity was cool, so Theodor never tried his most hilarious fun on her. But Caroline never could get enough of it.

142

Mary admired Caroline's ability to cook as well as James's mother, and Caroline was glad to teach Mary, apt pupil that she was. Caroline's face would light up as Mary—Mrs. James Cleaveland, wife of a sea captain—put on an apron in that old kitchen and asked advice.

Often when sportsmen came there, lured by good fishing in the mill stream and the reputation of Caroline Luce's cooking, Mary would set the table before the open fire, spread the red-and-white checked cloth, mix and cook the sour-milk corn bread, an art she had mastered completely, and transfer it, brown and appetizing, from the coals to the pewter plate. Caroline would add the trout, freshly caught, and newly roasted coffee. There was a breakfast for you!

And Mrs. James Cleaveland at Caroline's request would sit down at dinner and act as hostess. "Won't you have some more of this chicken, Mr. Smith? It's very nice." More and more often people came.

Now the young people of the village flocked to Mary's banner. Susan Vincent, Betsy Luce, and Nancy Allen, who had always liked her, now suggested that they start a series of quilting parties of their own. Usually young and old worked together at the quiltings, and the young people had to keep silent, listening to the dowagers or giggling under their breath. They'd have their own.

And Mary played hostess in Caroline's parlor, which Mary had decorated with feathery grasses and bright red berries. Caroline would bring in the tea and slices of bread, buttered on the loaf, cut thin, and served with strawberry jam, as Mary's mother used to do in Sydney. Caroline would have preferred cake. Some day Mary would have china of her own, thin and delicate and dainty.

Mary didn't see Saphronia again during the months that followed. She had gone to Boston to act as a companion and seamstress for some distant relative.

Many of the older women began to speak more pleasantly to Mary. Only a few, influenced by Mrs. Henry Cleaveland's superior position, kept their noses in the air.

28

MARY was out in the yard at Caroline Luce's that afternoon, digging around the rosebushes. Theodor had no use for posies and wouldn't spade up an inch of ground for anything but vegetables.

"We can make a flower garden ourselves, Caroline," Mary had said.

Sometimes "Uncle Willard," as the neighbors called the old man, came out to help, but this afternoon he had a "crick" in his back. Caroline was busy with the supper.

Mary dug in with the spade and leaned down. The earth smelled good, and in turning it over she seemed to lighten a burden within her. She hadn't heard from James for months, not since last summer. He was always in her mind. She could picture the *Mary Wilder* tossing in a heavy sea, rising to the tops of the waves and dipping. She could see James at the wheel. She could see him watching the sails and the clouds and the flight of sea birds. She could see his face light at a certain sound in the rigging that meant that the sails were drawing smoothly.

Now as she smelt the earth and heard the robins and bluebirds and saw the little leaflets coming out reddish-green above the thorns, she began to hum softly, and soon she was singing.

Whenever Mary straightened up her voice rose above the hissing of fat in the frying pan, so Caroline kept looking out and listening.

"She'd sing in spite of everything!" Caroline said to herself, and she kicked aside a chunk of firewood that in her mind represented Mrs. Henry Cleaveland. "And him not writing to her!" she said aloud.

"Hey?" queried Uncle Willard.

"He'd ought to write her a letter." Caroline raised her voice and indicated Mary singing out in the yard.

"Like enough he has wrote, Carrie," Willard's voice quavered. "It ain't every place has a mail system like this on', where you get the mail delivered as fast as the stage can make it up island from the boat. At least that was the way it used to be when I was a handlin' it. These ships, now. Sometimes they ain't in sight of land for two-three months. You can't depend on 'em! I don't know what in thunder anybody wants to go to sea for."

"A sailor does look handsome a jinglin' the coins in his pocket."

"Humph!" Uncle Willard snorted, but in spite of himself he added admiringly under his breath, "A sea cap'n does look handsome!"

1 4 6

"Say! Here comes the stage now!" Caroline put the frying pan to one side, wiped her hands on her apron, and went into the room that served as post office.

Uncle Willard was already ahead of her, even with the "crick" in his back.

"Pa," Caroline's sides shook with laughter, "if you ain't like a old rooster that sees a young cock headed off with his hens!"

"Hey?"

But Caroline didn't repeat her remark.

William Mayhew came in by the front door. It was his business to attend to the mail and to try to keep Uncle Willard in check. He unlocked the big canvas bag with a large key attached to his watch chain, and, putting on his spectacles, he leisurely took out letters and packages and newspapers and deliberately put them in their proper pigeonholes.

Uncle Willard watched him silently, sitting on the stool in front of the high desk where *he* had stood as postmaster so many years. The little office on the other side of the barrier began to fill with people.

Suddenly Willard's practiced eye discovered a packet addressed, "Mrs. Henry Cleaveland, Care Ship *Niger*."

"There, Carrie, What'd I tell y'u? He *has* wrote!"

William Mayhew looked up. "There is to be no tampering with the mails!" he said sternly.

"Humph! Who's a tamperin' with 'em? I tampered with mail when you was still in long skirts!" And turning to where his daughter-in-law had been standing, he ordered, "Tell Mary . . . " But Caroline was not there. She had already gone to find Mary.

I 4 7

Now Mary came in, her cheeks pink with spring wind and excitement, her eyes bright, her lips red, a scratch across her little nose where the rosebush had whipped against her, and her hair wind-blown.

A letter! But it was addressed to Mrs. Henry Cleaveland! It was lying there with others in a pile! Mr. Mayhew was picking it up, impersonally reading the address, and tucking it into the pigeonhole marked "Capt. Henry Cleaveland." Mary knew the packet contained letters for the families of members of the crew, letters for James's mother and sisters, and a letter for her. And Mary was afraid that hers might never be delivered. She must get in touch with someone, Daniel or Addie. Father and Sylvanus were at sea again.

"I vum if I wouldn't open it up and distribute the letters myself. It ain't an official seal on it." He could do it as well as not if he wasn't a scared.

"Mr. Luce," said Mr. Mayhew with dignity, "I'll thank you to keep out of my affairs." He moistened his thumb and slid another letter off the diminishing pack.

Uncle Willard hobbled off to the kitchen. "Carrie, this crick in my back's getting worse. Rub some of that wintergreen liniment on it, will y'u?"

"Some supper for the inside of y'u would be more to the point." Carrie replaced the frying pan over the coals. "Someday I'm goin' to have me a stove. One like Captain Marchant's wife's got."

Mary still lingered in the post office, forgetful of her earthy hands, her scratched face, her touseled hair, unconscious of looking like a pathetic little schoolgirl. That packet of letters! If she could only see it she'd know how James had fared on his voyage, if he was well, what he had seen and where he had been for almost a year. And—and perhaps she'd hear when he was coming home.

"Oh, here's Dan!" Her face lighted up. "Danny, Danny, look!" She pointed into the pigeonhole where the edges of the packet showed.

Daniel whistled. "'Bout time we heard!"

"Dan, couldn't you open up the packet? There'll be letters for other people in it, and you could deliver them right away."

"Think I'd open up Ma's mail? Don't you know Ma yet?"

"But my letter's in there!"

Several of the men standing near looked interested. Who was going to win out in this contest, they wondered.

Daniel edged Mary out through the back of the office and into the yard where they could talk. "Ma'll probably put your letter on the mantel and say, 'There! That's for Mary, when she has a mind to come for it!' And she'll emphasize the last few words, so nobody'll dare take it to you."

"Danny, *you'd* dare! And can you inquire around to find out when the *Mary Wilder* is expected in New Bedford? And when James comes, when James is expected—promise you'll take me to Holmes's Hole so I can meet him."

"Suppose Ma wants to go. . . . "

"Take me down the day before and leave me at Susan Cromwell's. She has always been nice to me from the moment I stepped ashore. I could spend the night with her."

"All right. I'll do it."

"Thank you." She kissed him gratefully. "Danny, bring me the letter if you can."

She went into the house where she saw in the little mirror against the kitchen wall that she looked quite disheveled. Quickly she smoothed her hair and washed up and then ate her supper thoughtfully. Who else, she wondered, would get letters from the *Mary Wilder*? But it wouldn't be fitting for her to inquire for the captain from the mother of the cabin boy. At any rate James was safe. She had seen his handwriting on the envelope.

29

UNAWARE that Mary was already there, Mrs. Cleaveland came down to the wharf and was seated in the carriage awaiting her son with plenty all ready to say to him. When Mary appeared with Susan Cromwell their greetings were answered in monosyllables, but Mary didn't notice. She was at peace with the world, for James was coming.

They watched the *Eagle's Wing*, the new steamer, come nosing around the point in her clean white paint, with shiny black funnel puffing smoke and yellow paddle wheels churning the water. The harbor was busy with little craft and a few small coastwise schooners with their noisy sailors. There was the *Eagle's Wing* with the big American flag hoisted clear to the top of the mast, a signal to all Vineyarders that there was a whaling captain aboard.

Mary stood there, quivering with happiness, prettier

than ever. The sumptuous, carefree meals at Caroline Luce's had made her plump but still dainty. The consciousness of her new-found ability allowed her to hold up her head with the best New England housewives. Every inch of her small stature showed the dignity of having asserted her rights and having won the respect and admiration of her fellows. It wasn't everybody that would have opposed the old tyrant!

The gangplank was scarcely lowered when Mary rushed through the crowd and up on it. A husky sailor was about to interfere, but the mate said, "Captain Cleaveland's wife. Let her come aboard."

"The bold huzzy!" muttered the captain's mother from her carriage on the wharf.

James was standing on the quarter-deck, ready to jump ashore. He wasn't so eager now that Mary was aboard, so this one and that one and the other one got ashore ahead of him. Mrs. Henry Cleaveland sat waiting in the carriage.

Mary rushed up to him, embraced him, wept over him. "James," she said, "take me with you the next voyage. I don't care if I am seasick all the time. I want to go with you."

James looked at her eager, upturned face, at her broad forehead, her deep blue-gray eyes, her nose with the piquant tilt, at her lips red from his kisses. Why not? Almy had promised him that big, new ship he was having built. It would be a long voyage, but the ship would be comfortable for a woman. Captain DeBlois and Captain Stanton had their wives on board with them. He'd often wished for Mary during the months he had been away.

"I should like that," he said, simply.

They went together to the carriage, where Mrs. Cleaveland sat, still frigid. James paid no attention but kept on talking until finally his geniality began to melt her reserve. He told briefly of the different ships he had seen, amusing anecdotes of this captain and that or stories concerning foreign ports, trivial tales to keep things of moment from the surface.

He had been challenged to a duel by some drunken Englishman in a South American port. He'd forgotten the details, for he hadn't paid much attention at the time, but the next day the man sent his second to call. Since James was the challenged party he could choose the weapons. " 'Whaling harpoons,' says I. Strange, I heard no more of the matter."

Mary thought, "How awful! What a narrow escape!"

But Mrs. Cleaveland laughed heartily. No need to fear for these sons of hers. Quick-witted, brave, handsome, they could look out for themselves, at least where men were concerned, or whales, or ships.

Then James asked for news of his own home, a question captains always dread and ask sadly, fearing that ill things might have happened during their long absences.

Mrs. Cleaveland answered that they had been well at her house. Daniel was doing nicely with his studies. Addie was a big, strong girl, and Eliza was married. Mary had been having a good time, she supposed, off by herself. She noticed there were always plenty of folks about her. She meant to say men were about her, but the look on James's face made her a little cautious.

"Yes," said Mary simply. "When you left it seemed as

though I wasn't wanted, so I went over to Caroline Luce's. It was better that way for everybody." Mary knew James would never comprehend the subtleties of his mother's cruelty, for she had always been kind to him.

James realized there were two strong wills at combat. "Just when Ma seemed to be in the lead," he said to himself, "Mary struck out and won. Spunky little critter!"

They were nearing home. There was the little tree-of-heaven shoot that Pa had brought from China, waving its feathery plume above the barn. It looked odd among all the chunky orchard trees.

"Well," said Mrs. Cleaveland, "I have a good dinner for you, James. I suppose Mary is eating at Caroline Luce's."

James was used to making quick decisions. He would look at the clouds and order all sail taken in but a double-reefed tops'l, or he'd crowd on sail to take advantage of the trades. He had seen fights among the men and had stopped them. These women's messes were different, but he could see a need for action, definite and swift.

"I am coming home, Ma, and my wife comes with me."

30

FORTUNATELY for Mary, the stay with her mother-in-law was not long this time, for James had always wanted Squire George's house, and now that he had the money to buy it he and his wife could settle there until they went to sea. He had never liked the idea of the house being in other hands. Jimmy Jones had raised hob with the family fortunes. First he married Aunt Avis and dissipated all her money and her father's money. Then when she died he sold the house out of the family and went off to Philadelphia to run a newspaper and contract more debts, most likely. Maybe you could stand having a writer in the family if ever he could keep out of the poorhouse or out of jail. He would arrange with Joseph and Eliza Nickerson to buy the place immediately. They could stay upstairs until they found other quarters.

Mary was delighted with having a house of her own, just she and James together. Several times they went to

Holmes's Hole to buy additional things, spending the day with James's cousins, the Cromwells or the Claghorns or the Cleavelands.

"And now," thought Mary, as they moved in, "I'll surprise James with my cooking." Without saying a word to James she bought a fowl from Caroline Luce, plucked it and dressed it as she had seen Caroline do, cut it up with a little cleaver, browned it in its own fat, then simmered it till it was tender. She had fresh vegetables from the Nickerson garden. She made shortcake, cooked it brown, and finished with a huckleberry pie. It was a dinner fit for a king, the first real meal she had ever cooked for James.

Mary waited breathlessly for James to say, "I didn't know you could cook like this!" But not a word! He passed his plate for a second helping and went on discussing the topics of the day.

"They say Jimmy Jones died of cholera in Brooklyn. He didn't last long after Aunt Avis. Served him right, too. There's cholera in New York, seventy cases in Boston, cholera in Fall River. The Isthmus is full of it, but they don't mean to have it here. The Board of Health in Edgartown won't let a ship get within a hundred fathoms of any wharf if she's even had the smell of port where there is contagion. They can't throw things overboard from ships, and everyone in town has to clean out his cesspools and outbuildings. Some folks have to be scared into making things shipshape."

"Was there any fever in Talcahuano when you were there?" Mary asked fearfully.

"I didn't run across any cases, but there are so many

FRENCH TOBACCO JAR
SCRIMSHAW BODKIN
SCRIMSHAW SWIFT

*Old map of Dukes County, Nantucket,
and Barnstable counties. Rosewood table
given to James by his mother when he
first "set up housekeeping."*

half-made foreigners around you never know what they might have.

"The Russians are cutting up again at Gallipoli and Odessa. It seems as if there was always some sort of a war brewing. It's bad for whaling if they go too far with it."

James passed his plate a third time.

"There was considerable talk about annexing the Sandwich Islands. It would be the best thing that could happen. With one or two hundred whalers stopping there at a time between seasons, it means pretty good business for them, and it's a fine place for the ships to stop. It wouldn't be so good if the French took possession of the islands, as they have been threatening. The French are no colonizers. Hard people to deal with.

"Once I took forty Frenchmen off a wreck in the Okhotsk Sea. They jabbered away and got under foot so I could scarcely sail the ship. One of them gave me that tobacco jar, but not even a letter of thanks from the French government. It's no small matter feeding forty men at sea when you have only enough for your own crew."

James passed his plate again.

Mary could restrain herself no longer. "Do you like the dinner, James?"

"To be sure," he answered nonchalantly.

It was a good thing Caroline had taught her to cook, Mary concluded, for James expected good food on shore.

In the evening they sat out on the west step together. They could hear the Nickerson children talking and playing. When they were having their supper Mary heard one of the little boys call, "Ma, more saleratus."

1 5 7

Poor Mrs. Nickerson had to do something to make that sour milk palatable. It never kept in this weather unless it was put down the well.

Mrs. Nickerson was a lovely woman, one of a large family of minister's children, well educated and pleasant spoken, but her husband was as stubborn as a mule. James said the Nickersons didn't belong here. "They came from off, from the Cape somewhere. David Look brought 'em all here, quantities of 'em, when he married Hannah."

They looked out across fields to the other part of the village. They could see teams driving up to Nathan Mayhew's store to be tied at the stone hitching posts. Nathan's house was opposite, snuggled into the apple orchard. Further on was William Athearn's "Traveler's Home," the Chase house, the Academy, and the blacksmith shop—all on the other side of the brook. Beyond were the Chilmark Hills—Goat Pasture, Peaked Hill, and Prospect. The sun would set behind the ones further north, but not for quite a long time in these summer evenings.

Tonight they had walked to the post office together, and as it was Friday they came back with the *Gazette*. James was eager to open it. "That little paper used to be handled like so much precious metal, if we ever got one from some ship that had received mail. Sometimes they were left at the Galápagos mailbox. The sailors nearly always stop there for fresh meat and fruits, so they rigged up this arrangement for mail. I've found all kinds of local newspapers there, read 'em all, and put 'em back for the next fellow. Sometimes I've found letters there waiting for me and just kind of hoping I'd be along." James filled his pipe and settled down.

Mary sat beside him with her sewing. The wind that had been blowing hot and dry all the afternoon had calmed until now the leaves of the trees barely fluttered; a robin was singing his good-night song; little night insects were beginning to tune up; the early evening dampness brought out the pungent smell of the mayweed. James puffed at his pipe, turning the paper occasionally, making brief comments. Suddenly he sat up. "Look here, Mary! Look at this! Captain Jernegan got that fellow!"

Mary dropped her work, "What fellow?"

James read from the *Gazette:* "Captured at last! *Rebecca Sims,* New Bedford, captures whale five months after *Ann Alexander* was sunk, with two harpoons in him marked *Ann Alexander.* Whale's head seriously injured, and contained pieces of ship's timbers. He had lost his wildness and ferocity, being very much diseased, but upon being taken yielded seventy or eighty barrels of oil!"

"There you have it. He got his come-uppance for sinking that ship."

"How could a whale sink a ship?" asked Mary.

"He was a bad one! The critter stove two boats, smashed them to atoms. The crew managed to get aboard the *Ann Alexander.* Then Captain DeBlois chased the whale with the ship, but the whale came for them first and stove a great hole in her abreast the foremast. The wonder is they lived to tell the tale."

"What did they do, at sea without any ship?"

"They took to their boats, the two that were left, got hold of the chronometer, charts, and sextant, as many provisions as possible, which wasn't much, and a very little water. They headed for the rainy latitudes.

"As luck would have it the ship *Nantucket*, Captain Gibbs, came along, and rescued them. Took them to Paita, where the captain entered his protest."

"Protest against a whale?"

"That's what they call it when you tell the consul what's happened to your ship. It was due to the captain's clear thinking that no lives were lost. A brave man and a just one! When he considered the ship doomed he was the only one to go aboard her, and he alone cut down the masts with the hope of righting her. He lives up to sea traditions. There are few whalers that don't have courage and sense, though some of the rough fellows give us a bad name in port."

The sun had set while they were talking. A few lights shone in the village. A dog barked in the distance. A little screech owl called plaintively. A June bug zoomed around, then dropped with a heavy thud. A bird repeated, "Whip-poor-will, whip-poor-will, whip-poor-will."

James picked up his paper and his pipe. "Time to go in, Mary!"

He put his arm around her, and stood looking down into her eyes.

"Mary, do you like it?" he asked, indicating the big old house.

She reached up to him, putting both hands on his shoulders. "It's like being bride and groom, to be sure, having a place of our own, just to ourselves."

James held her close and kissed her, and then on a

sudden impulse he swung her clear of the ground into his arms and carried her over the threshold of their home.

The summer passed quickly in working around the house and garden, tending to the little pigs and chickens, going to Holmes's Hole with James, going on picnics with the other young people of the village to the South Beach, where they held sailboat races on the Great Pond, with clambakes at noon. They rode out to call on the neighbors. Sometimes they went as far as Edgartown, the county seat. Oldtown, James called it, because it was the first to be settled on the Island.

In September there was a gale that drove the bark *Mary Sawyer* ashore on the South Side. She'd come from Rio de Janeiro with a load of rosewood and coffee. They got the ship off, finally, but not before one poor fellow was drowned trying to reach the shore.

A little later the steamer *Arctic* collided with a British troopship. Only 30 passengers out of 300 were saved. It was feared Captain Luce had been lost, but he was rescued later. It was said that when Captain West of the *Atlantic* heard the news, he leaped on the paddle box, fairly dancing with emotion as he roared out, "Hurrah, boys, three cheers for the safety of Captain Luce!"

One of James's friends from Holmes's Hole stopped to talk about the slave that escaped from the bark *Franklin*, landed on West Chop, and got to a swamp in Gay Head. Sheriff Lambert went after him with a warrant, but they didn't suppose he searched very hard. He wouldn't be very diligent after slaves. As soon as his back was turned two women drove up in a buggy with food and women's clothes. They went into the swamp, fed and disguised the slave, then took him to Menemsha, where he went by boat to the home of an abolitionist in New Bedford.

As the weather grew cold, James piled the woodshed high with heavy logs and left sticks in big hutlike piles in the yard. Mary often went with him on his trips to the wood lot.

They started Daniel off to medical school in Brunswick, Maine.

In November Caroline Luce had her baby, a boy. Mary went often to see her, to take her delicacies and talk to her. Caroline's sister Sarey Ann was with her as nurse, and her mother, who soon earned the name Aunt Rhody in the village.

That winter Mayhew Look and Eliza Vincent were married by the Reverend Jesse Pease. Mayhew Look had promised to sail as first mate on James's next voyage. "It will be hard for that woman, left alone," thought Mary.

They were glad the wood was piled high. Mary hurried with the quilt she was making. Some of the young women came in to help her. Ice formed in the hen dishes every morning, clinking against the sides as she moved them.

James had his pigs killed and salted down. The hams and shoulders he had smoked and hung from the rafters in the big kitchen. He bought half a bullock, froze it, and carried it up to the attic. He'd hack off pieces of it later, thaw them out, and they'd have fresh meat all winter. He filled the cellar with potatoes, turnips, cabbages, beets, carrots, and onions. Mary peeled apples, strung them on threads, and hung festoons of them out against the woodhouse door to dry.

In the evenings they sat in the kitchen with the doors closed. The great fireplace swallowed up cordwood sticks. They moved their chairs closer and put Great-grandfather George Athearn's warming pan close by, ready for the hot coals that were to warm their bed. Mary loved to sit here warm by the fire, though sometimes she did wish there were more people to drop in. She missed the laughter and chatter of a big family. James did, too, and sometimes would ask Mary to go over to Mother's for the evening. She didn't mind as long as James was with her.

In January the big snowstorm came. There hadn't been one like it as long as James could remember.

For days the ocean moaned and moaned. The sky looked leaden. James said there would be a storm. Then the snow came in little pellets, hitting hard against the windows. A little later, when Mary looked up from her work, it was thick and gray and coming down faster and faster. The woods in the distance looked like a faint line of purple. The weedstalks in the yard stood out like starry flowers.

James moved about restlessly, making sure that everything was shipshape.

Then the wind rose and howled around the house. Snow dropped down the chimney and hissed in the fire. For several days it kept on coming, sometimes with sharp, metallic noises, then settling down softly and gently. When the snow stopped the wind whipped it into queer-shaped drifts like little gnomes' houses. They walked through the Case place, right over the tops of the fences, through the orchard, up to Mrs. Cleaveland's east door.

It was colder than the other winters, James said. It was the coldest he'd ever seen. Mrs. Cleaveland said it was because they were living in that ramshackle old house. But Mary didn't mind the cold that year. Her cheeks were full and pink, her eyes sparkled, and she sang continually about the house.

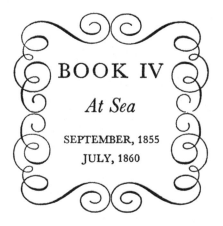

BOOK IV

At Sea

SEPTEMBER, 1855
JULY, 1860

31

As the *Eagle's Wing* plowed into the harbor past the fort on Clark's Point she gave a shrill blast from her whistle as if to proclaim to the mute sailing vessels that here was progress and hustle. She frothed along with her paddle wheels clunking rhythmically and her walking beam rising and falling. Black smoke billowed behind and trailed away with the creaming blue-white wake.

They passed the bark *Alabama*, that had been towed into port for repairs a few days ago, and the bark *Alice Frazier*, newly arrived from the Pacific Ocean. James knew her master, Captain Taber. He seemed to know each vessel from way off, while Mary had to read the name under the counter.

"You can tell a vessel by the 'cut of her jib,' " James told her.

Alongside Commercial Wharf were a dozen or more ships—whalers loading and unloading. The sound of

167

mallets could be heard as the coopers walked around their casks and tapped the hoops in place. Oil trucks with wide wheels rumbled from the wharf, loaded; drays were arriving with provisions and stores. Men were in the rigging, on deck, on the docks, everywhere. All seemed bent on rendering service to the whale ships, as if the very life of the port depended upon them, as indeed it did.

"Look, Mary, there's the *Seconet*. By George, she does look shipshape!"

Mary had never seen James so excited, so much like a boy. She saw that he was watching the trim vessel being provisioned at a near-by wharf. She noticed the white canvas, the new paint and cordage, the shining masts and spars.

"Four hundred tons," he told her. "That's a good-sized ship. Come on, Mary! This steamer's swung clear. Let's get ashore!"

James picked up the carpet bag and with Mary's hand on his arm went up the narrow gangplank to the dock. Edwin Williams Athearn was there to meet them. He took the captain's bag and led the way to a waiting hack. It was only a short drive, but the narrow, hilly street was so choked with drays and great straining horses that they made slow progress. The sidewalks were cluttered with baskets of vegetables and burlap-covered barrels. Nearly every corner on Union Street housed an outfitter's establishment or a grogshop. Rough men loitered there and exchanged coarse repartee with the draymen, with the shopkeepers—with anyone who came their way. To Mary it looked as if there were no law and one must take his life in his hands to try to pass on foot. She was glad when the hack pulled up before the Mansion House, which nearly all the sea captains made their headquarters.

Mary had been married to James for nearly four years now, but it still seemed wonderful to see him write in his fine, strong hand, "James F. Cleaveland and Wife." They talked to the proprietor for a while, then they were shown upstairs.

Their room was very nice. From the windows Mary could see the masts in the harbor, a strip of blue water, and the pretty town of Fairhaven across the bay. The red carpet looked new. Fresh towels hung on the painted rack, and the washbowl and pitcher were neatly concealed in a chest of drawers. There was a little vase of flowers and a china pitcher that held some cold water and tinkling ice. What a treat on a hot forenoon!

"Make yourself at home," said James, "while I go over to the customhouse to see about my papers. We may be able to get them through in time to sail on the afternoon tide. High water is about five, and we can sail soon after that."

James hurried out while Mary took up her bag to unpack a few things and rearrange her hair. Before she had finished, the smell of browning meat reminded her that it was nearly noon. She was hungry, and the thought of someone else's food appealed to her. Hotel cooking was seldom as good as home fare, but it was different, and she liked new things.

Mary was ready when James returned. Together they went to the dining room. The dinner was fine, flavored nicely and well served, but Mary was too excited to eat heartily.

"Fill up, Mary," James suggested. "You won't get such another chance."

Mary looked up quickly. Yes, James was serious. It was true. She had forgotten the monotony of sea fare, the hunger for green things, for vegetables of any kind, for fruit. On the *Emma Prescott* she had longed for an apple, an orange, a raw potato even. And during the six months on board the *Mary Wilder* she had become thoroughly sick of salt meat.

James continued eating, talking meanwhile. "I had to wait at the customhouse while Captain Cook of the *Canton* mulled things over. He's sailing on this afternoon's tide. And then there was all this extra red tape on account of this being the maiden voyage of the *Seconet*. Almy's real pleased with her. He has a model of her in his office, and he expects good work from her. She's faster'n most whalers—yet she has the storage space, too."

"Almy? Oh, the owner."

"Yes. I told Almy I'd ship oil back as fast as I got it. It won't be so bad with you along, Mary—it won't be so bad staying away five or six years."

Five or six years! "Oh, God!" she whispered.

"What say?"

"James, I was praying, praying I could keep up my courage." Five or six years on a whaler! "I hadn't thought it would be so long."

"Well, you wanted to come!" And then more gently, "You'll be going ashore now and again, as often as we hit port."

"New Bedford to Honolulu—six months!" And then, as if to keep up her spirits, "But 'twas nice there."

"We're not going there this time."

"But where—Oh, James, I didn't mean to complain. I thought it would be two years, perhaps."

"Mary," James leaned forward, and spoke earnestly. "You'll be treated well on board that vessel. You'll be the same as a queen. You won't have to contend with victuals and housecleaning. That'll all be taken care of. You won't hear an oath or any dirty talk. If I ever heard a complaint on that score I'd whale the tar out of the son of a . . . . Say! There's Edwin Williams looking for me. Time we started."

Mary had hoped for a chance to visit the shops, but she dutifully went upstairs to gather up her belongings while James strode off to the water front and his ship.

"I'll have Edwin Williams get you a hack," he said.

In a short time the boy returned. "I ain't had time to get slicked up," he apologized. "I was a loadin' ship when Mr. Look sent me to fetch the cap'n. It don't look as if we was goin' to get off today."

Edwin Williams was proud to be considered an able-bodied seaman at fifteen. He had been cabin boy on the last voyage of the *Mary Wilder*, and the crew list made him fifteen three years ago, though his neighbors in West Tisbury had known he was only a little over twelve. The Cleavelands felt responsible for him, because his father had been swept overboard from the *Luminary* and lost during a gale.

At the dock there was great activity. A fussy little tug was towing the *Canton* out into midstream. There were girls on the wharf waving to the sailors, but Mary didn't like their looks. She sat with straightened back and eyes averted. Then she heard the familiar voice of Mayhew Look, a neighbor in West Tisbury and first mate of the *Seconet*.

"Those provisions ain't up to standard," he shouted angrily. "Cap'n Cleaveland wouldn't feed 'em to a self-respectin' hog."

They had to wait until the next day for other supplies.

Six years! It was just chance that Mr. Look had discovered those provisions. They might have set out for a six-year voyage with food not fit for hogs.

Six years! Six years ago she was less than sixteen. She wasn't married. She hadn't even thought of singing in San Francisco. She hadn't left home. Six years from now she'd be sunburned and salt-incrusted—an old woman.

But she had chosen this life. She would accept it with good grace, "never looking backward!"

And she'd be with James, her husband.

She'd be queen on the *Seconet*.

And she'd have a chance tomorrow to do some shopping in New Bedford.

32

I⊤ was daylight. Mary and James were aware of it,
although there were no sounds of birds, no cool breeze
to move the window shade. Instead of meadow larks and
song sparrows there was a dull rumbling of drays on
cobbles. A sultry smell of fog-drenched buildings, fish
wharves, and cookery assailed their nostrils. Across
Buzzard's Bay a sulphurous glow showed where the sun
was wrestling with the thin fog.

They both felt a sense of loss because there were no
daily chores to do. They felt as though they were visiting.
They talked quietly, experimentally, lest they wake
someone, then naturally. They reviewed plans for the
years ahead of them. Had they everything necessary—
books, writing materials, sewing?

James always carried his Bible—every captain had one
on his ship—a book of sermons for service Sunday mornings, some bound copies of Littel's *Living Age*, Horsburg's
Guide, and a few others.

"Wouldn't you like to buy some books to take along, Mary? Life won't be dull on board if you can enjoy your mind."

Mary thought seriously about the reading problem. She had been brought up in a large family in which she seldom had to think of her own entertainment, and there had been little time for reading. At the Vineyard the Cleavelands had read a great deal, and whenever she went to Deacon Cottle's the pleasure of books had been made real to her.

"Yes, I'd like some books," she said.

After breakfast James set out for the water front. Mary waited until she felt sure the shops would be open, then set forth to make her purchases. All the life seemed to be draining downhill toward the harbor. Purchase Street was quiet. To Mary this was the middle of the morning, but to the merchants it was not yet opening time.

Soon things began to stir and brighten. Window shades were raised; a tradesman whistled; a proprietor swept the sidewalk in front of his place. Mary went into a dry-goods store to buy bright-colored ribbons, some yarn for knitting, and thread for crocheting.

Around on Union Street she found a bookseller's, Parsons and Company. There she purchased the current magazines—*Harper's, Frank Leslie's Gazette, Godey's Lady's Book*, the *New York Journal*. The books looked inviting, and she bought a few. *The Hidden Path*, by Marian Harland, was rather expensive, but the title was appealing. *Confessions of a Pretty Woman*, by Miss Pardoe, and *A Jealous Wife*, by the same author, were cheaper, yet they promised much.

174

By this time New Bedford proper had awakened, and everyone seemed to be hurrying about his business. Mary took her packages under her arm. She wouldn't accept the offer to have them delivered to the hotel, for she was afraid she would never see them again.

She strolled along Main Street. It was a pleasure to be able to walk along a city street. She watched the shops, the people, the traffic. Saddle horses were few, but wheeled vehicles were everywhere. The air was soft and moist and free from dust. How strange that she should be making these comparisons with Sydney as soon as she felt paving beneath her feet. It had been five years since she had left Australian soil and she felt thoroughly American, yet here she was striving to catch, in the bustle of New Bedford, other sounds and sights.

That afternoon she set out with James, well content this time to leave the city. As they started down Union Street Mary wished they might walk. She felt sick from the pitching of the hack.

"James, can't we get out and walk?"

"What in thunder do you want to get out and walk for?" But he looked at her white face and climbed down quickly. Helping her over the high wheel, he carried her across the cobbled street to the sidewalk. He set her on her feet and looked at her in dismay. "This bodes ill for a voyage in rough waters," he said.

"I'll feel all right if I stay out in the air," she said weakly, though she herself had a presentiment that this wouldn't be the only time she'd feel sick.

They walked slowly along the narrow sidewalks that were unbelievably dirty and littered with refuse from the commission markets. The workers had little regard for pedestrians and tugged at their bales and crates with sharp, swinging hooks. Three rough-looking sailors lurched around the corner almost into James and Mary. Mary could feel her husband's arm stiffen in readiness for anything, but the men straightened up, touched their caps, and stood one side.

When they reached the wharf the *Seconet* was not in sight. "She's out at Clark's Point awaiting the tide. We'll go out in the pilot's boat just before she weighs anchor," James explained. "A master wants to stay ashore until she's loaded. Interferes with the mate's authority."

"Here's Mr. Pierce, now!" They climbed aboard his sailboat and went out to the *Seconet*. She loomed up big above them as the pilot's boat came alongside.

"Lower your ladder, Mr. Look," James shouted.

It sounded strange. At home on the Vineyard he'd said Mayhew Look this and Mayhew that, but now she could see that James would have no familiarity. His brother had been Mr. Cleaveland on board the *Mary Wilder*. On shipboard an officer was Mister.

It was fortunate that Mary was young and lithe. She climbed up the rope ladder easily and only took Mr. Look's hand in courtesy as he offered to help her to the deck.

What a scene of confusion greeted her! Everything was piled on deck—provisions, baggage, stores, and equipment. Much to Mary's surprise, it didn't seem to trouble James. He hadn't yet assumed responsibility.

She watched the crew as they worked ineffectively. She had expected to see a rough lot but found instead that they were only boys. Some were the neighbors' children. She recognized William West, Richard Look, and William Waldron besides Edwin Williams Athearn. James let her see the crew list, and she noticed that most of them were as young as or younger than she. From the list of thirty-one there was only one man—James R. Fordham from Connecticut, the fourth mate, thirty-seven, who was older than James, the captain, who was thirty-two. None of the others exceeded twenty-five years. Many of them were green hands but were soon to learn that when James gave an order they were to run and do something. What to do they would soon find out from experience.

She had hardly gone to her cabin down a steep, narrow stair, or ladder, when she heard the pilot giving instructions to unfurl the sails, then hoist the anchor. She returned to the deck to see the men walking around the capstan, pushing at the heavy bars. Someone struck up a chantey that fitted the tramping feet and clicking dogs. The vessel was already in motion when the pilot gave orders that brought the sails to the wind. The *Seconet* was on her way.

There was an easy swing that promised good sailing qualities for this new ship. The breeze came down cool from the swelling white canvas. New Bedford slowly dwindled on her starboard quarter as the sun sank in a ruddy haze—a crimson ball.

"Red sky at night, sailor's delight," came to Mary's mind as the ship sailed on.

The lingering twilight was still with them when they steered into the narrow channel of Quicks's Hole, between Nashawena and Pasque islands. Off to the starboard Mary could see a white crescent beach and on the other side of the channel the rugged shrub-lined shore of little Pasque. The tide from Buzzard's Bay made out so rapidly that the *Seconet* rushed through, and then they were out in the open sea.

James pointed out the dark mass of the Vineyard with No Mans Land lying beyond. In the gathering darkness Mary looked at her island home and the flashing red and white beams from Gay Head Light.

It was too late to see anything but stars and this guiding beacon. Soon the pilot would relinquish his charge of the *Seconet*, and then James would steer her out into the velvety blackness.

Mary went to bed and lay there listening. She heard the pilot leave in his small sailboat. His parting words were muffled by the sea sounds—the lapping waves, the creaking cordage, the surf on the distant island.

33

MARY stretched and turned over sleepily—and then sat up with a start. Now she remembered. She was at sea. There was a pleasant sloshing of water and a hum in the rigging. She lay down once more. Her bed swayed slightly in its gimbals. Overhead the needle of the telltale compass held steadily south-southeast, just trembling with the motion of the ship. She was directly under it—in James's place.

She looked around the snug stateroom. Every inch of space was utilized—for closets, for seats, for a table. Over the bed there were firearms in a rack. At the foot was a picture of two orphans gazing with sad eyes at a little portrait of their mother. There was another picture on the side wall—a beautiful lady, dressed poorly. Her tragic eyes met Mary's whenever she looked up.

James must have gone on deck early. How soundly she had slept not to hear him when he got up or when he came to bed last night! Why, where was he? His side of the bed was unwrinkled except where she herself had slid over there just now. There was no mark on his pillow—no hollow where his head had lain.

Quickly she rubbed the sleep out of her eyes, smoothed the waves of her hair with both hands, and adjusted her nightdress. James was coming.

"Good morning, Mary."

"Good morning, Cap'n." She had heard about the sailor who was knocked down by Captain Mellen because he hadn't said, "Good morning, Cap'n," as he passed on his round of duties.

James smiled. His teeth shone white from his dark beard. As he took off his captain's cap Mary could see how the tight band of it kept his hair in order, but she also saw that his eyes were tired.

"James, you haven't slept at all!"

"Can't say as I have."

"Isn't there anybody you can trust to spell you off?"

"First night out, Mary, and the watches not chosen. We'll get things in order today. I'll have this crew whipped into shape in no time."

"Whipped?" Mary questioned in horror, having heard some hair-raising stories of cruelty. Would James, too, use the same methods?

James didn't hear her, for he had opened a door that exposed a small washroom with all toilet accommodations fitted firmly to the wall. He was splashing vigorously. "Got plenty of water now. We may have to go easy later when the casks begin to fill with oil."

180

"I didn't know there was a washroom there. I used the one down the hall last night."

James laughed, blowing the soapsuds from his mouth. "Hall!" he exclaimed scornfully. "What do you think this is—a hotel?"

"No, the queen's palace."

James realized that she had scored a point, but he kept on. "You'll be calling the deck a roof, if I don't teach you better, and the ladder stairs. Hall! That's the companionway. And you've been using the officers' washroom. They don't want women in there."

"All right," Mary said meekly. "I won't go there again. This is much better, anyway."

James came back into the cabin combed, washed, refreshed. His eyes looked happy in spite of his lack of rest.

"I'm going to lie down for a few minutes."

"I'll dress quickly and go into the other cabin."

"No, no. Stay here. I like to feel you are near."

Mary smiled. It was nice to be wanted like that. "I'll keep very quiet."

"No need. You couldn't wake me now if you tromped around and shouted. But just let that needle veer and I'd be on deck quicker'n you could hook onto a snatch block."

"You couldn't see it if you were asleep."

"No need. I'd feel it."

"Oh!"

"You think strange, but it's kind of born with you—knowing sea things. Most islanders have an extra sense that way, hearing the sea all the time the way they do and feeling it and watching the turn of a wave and . . . "

His voice trailed off sleepily.

34

For days Mary was absorbed in the newness of things. She sat on the deck in the warm September sun watching the doings on the ship—the sailors scrubbing the deck, winding coils of rope, sharpening tools, and placing them in certain definite positions in the whaleboats stowed on deck. She sat looking out at the sea, out and out at the endless sea. There was nothing in sight except the undulating waves—green or blue or transparent as the sunlight varied.

The decks were cleared the second day out. James called all hands on deck, told the mates to choose their men, and stood by while first Mr. Look and then Mr. Adams picked the ones who looked the sturdiest or most resilient, or men they knew to have good qualities.

"Like choosing sides for a game," Mary thought.

The captain called them to attention—first the starboard watch and then the larboard.

Mary watched him as he paced up and down before the two groups, eyeing them critically; then he stood before them, tilting back on his heels and forward again.

"We have set out on a long voyage," he said, "with one object in view—to catch whales. Our owners have invested a large sum of money in this vessel. She's a good ship, provisioned with the best to be had. I shall keep her as well stocked as possible, but if things don't suit we'll have no grumbling. There's to be no profanity, no card-playing. Do your work and obey your officers, if you want to avoid trouble." His voice boomed out, emphasizing his prohibitions.

The men knew he meant what he said.

They could no longer see land, and a steady breeze sent the *Seconet* along.

"She's a clean sailer," James said, "with her freshly coppered hull and neat lines. Ballasted and trimmed so she sails smoother'n the *Mary Wilder*."

Mary would sit on the deck to watch the sailors work. They accepted her impersonally with a "Good day, ma'am," or a touch to the cap.

James said no ship he'd ever sailed on had been so neat. "I tell you, it takes a woman's eyes to get 'em spruced up." Not that Mary ever said a word. She knew that interference with, or suggestion about, the working of the ship would not be tolerated. It was simply her presence.

After unpacking her clothes Mary had put them away in the spaces alloted. She had made little curtains for the portholes with some of the bolt of muslin she had brought with her and a ruffled cover for the top of the chest of drawers. She had cut red flowers from an old strip of cloth to decorate them. This morning, now that she'd hung them, she'd read for a while.

Reading had never held much fascination for her. She loved conversation and music, but books were a last resort after a period of boredom. Now, however, it was dull on deck, and she had finished her work, so she took out the package that held the New Bedford purchases— books, magazines, writing paper. The magazines were real nice. She would read each story later. *Confessions of a Pretty Woman* sounded vain and *A Jealous Wife* not quite the thing, but since she had no other books she took them into the cabin to read.

It was a cozy place, with low beamed ceiling and a row of square windows in the stern. The light came in over her shoulder as she sat on the horsehair sofa to read. Reflections from the waves came through the muslin curtains and danced on the glossy paint. She could hear James walking back and forth on the poop deck overhead.

Opening one of her books she glanced through the pages. Why did she ever buy such a book as that? James would probably laugh at her and at the titles. Later, when he came in, she covered the books with her apron.

"Reading, Mary? I almost forgot something I bought for you in New Bedford." With this he reached into his sea chest for a parcel. "Here," he said, handing them to her. "I hope you'll like them." Then he went back on deck.

Mary opened the package, and there were two neat, brown volumes lettered in gold, *Queechy*, by Elizabeth Wetherill. She hastily put away Miss Pardoe's works and started with James's gift. Each day she read the books, and time and again she would go back and read over certain passages, entranced with the beautiful character of the heroine and amused with the humor of the book. Later she discovered the two discarded books and without further thought she knelt on the horsehair sofa, pushed open a window, and dropped them into the sea. It was a satisfaction to see them spread-eagle into the water and bob in the vessel's wake. The yellow cover of one remained in sight for a long time, but finally sank. She never knew whether the books were really good or not. It was sufficient to know that she was rather ashamed of her taste.

They were bound for Fayal in the Azores, she learned. Mary thought they were to go around the Horn. No one thought it worth while to tell her of the plans, so she had to piece out information from scraps of conversation and from direct questioning.

"James," Mary had asked, "if we aren't going to Honolulu, where *are* we going?"

"Cruising," James answered shortly.

"Oh!"

And again. "Don't we stop anywhere?"

"See any place to stop?"

"Well, I thought . . . "

"This is a whaling voyage, Mary. We'll slow down and stop, too, by George, if we catch a whale, till we get him hauled on board, tried out, and stowed down. Then we'll go on again, just roaming the sea."

"Oh!"

"See that man in the masthead?"

"Yes."

"Know what he's up to?"

"Isn't he watching to see how to steer the ship?"

"*I'm* watching to see how to steer the ship! He's watching for whales. If he sees so much as a plume of water he'll let us know, and we'll give chase if we have to bring her about."

"Even if we have to go in the other direction?"

"Yes, *ma'am!* Whaling's our purpose."

But a few days later James told her, "We'll be stopping at Fayal, likely."

Mary didn't know where it was. She wouldn't ask, but James took her over to the big chart on the wall back of the wheel. "See," he said. "These islands here, the Azores, make a good stopping place . . . gives the men a change. . . . "

"Me, too," Mary couldn't help saying.

James looked at her quietly. "There'll be longer cruises than this ahead, Mary."

"Oh, I know. We're after whales," she said quickly.

"There are good whaling grounds 200 or so miles below the Azores, and while we're in the neighborhood we'll get a chance to stretch our legs and get some fresh food."

"Mm," said Mary carefully.

"And I'll need a couple of extra hands, too."

"Sailors?"

"Yes. I'll get two-three Portugees there."

"What do you need any more for, James? They're falling all over each other as it is—and they're idle most of the time . . . "

186

Mary stopped, for she could see that James was angry.

"Look at here," he said. "Nobody tells me on board my own ship how to manage it." And then more gently, "If the Queen of England or the President of the United States stood there and gave orders, I'd say, 'Stand clear, madam. Stand clear, sir. A ship's a ship, and I'm master on board.' "

"I was just asking," Mary said meekly.

"You'll see what they're needed for when we start catching whales. This isn't like sailing the *Mary Wilder* home with a load of freight. This means business."

In the meantime they cruised along. "You're getting to be quite a sailor, Mary. You haven't been sick at all."

"No." Still she longed to do something, anything, to vary the monotony of this life.

Then suddenly, "Blooooooooows!" shouted James right beside her.

The man in the masthead looked startled. He'd been keeping a strict watch, to the starboard, to the larboard, fore and aft. He hadn't seen a sign of a whale, and yet the captain was shouting up to him, "Look alive there. What's the matter with you?" Still he couldn't see any plume of water or any great black back humping out of the sea.

At the first sound of that magic word the deck swarmed with men pushing and shouting at each other. Captain Cleaveland gave orders to bring the *Seconet* into the wind. With familiar commands he restored discipline; then he ordered the boats lowered.

Mary looked in vain for the whale. Even the officers

apparently hadn't seen it. Nor had the captain. He blew a whistle to recall the boats. "What did you let the critter get out of sight for?" he said, but his eyes twinkled. It was just a drill.

"Not often you have a drill on board a whaler," he explained to Mary, "but I've got a good many greenhorns here, and I want to be set when a whale heaves in sight."

The men took the hint and sharpened their harpoons. They spent long hours getting the heft of their weapons. The boat steerers coiled and recoiled the rope in their line tubs. Each day the mates checked on the implements lined up in the whaleboats so that everything would be at hand.

Before they had a chance to try their luck, however, on September 22, they sighted the green cone of Pico Alto smoking off the starboard bow. And soon the ship sailed in to the harbor of Fayal, where several large ships and many smaller ones were moored.

Mary watched excitedly. Land! A chance to go ashore —to smell the land smells, to touch growing things, to eat smooth fresh fruit, and talk with other women.

35

Mary awoke early the next morning. Everything was quiet on board the *Seconet*. There was no straining of planking, no pulling of cordage, no curling of foamy wake at the stern—just a gentle motion as the ship rode at anchor.

They would be going ashore today. A gay little tune kept repeating itself in her mind as she dressed. She'd put on the gray broadcloth with the bonnet that matched. She hurried, for she did not want to miss seeing the movements of other ships in the harbor—the early morning light shining on the pretty town of Fayal, the fishing boats in the harbor with the small friendly fishermen grinning up at them, trying to talk in spite of the barrier of a strange language. She coiled her hair in a knot at her neck and was ready when the cabin boy called her to breakfast.

She was getting accustomed now to their meals, where

she and James sat down together and started eating before the others joined them.

"Why don't they come when they are called?" she had asked.

"That's manners on board a whaler," James told her. "Mr. Look and Mr. Adams wouldn't sit down before the captain got started if they were starving to death—and the others sit down after them. You've got to have manners the same as in any other society."

And Mary noticed that on deck there seemed to be certain unwritten laws. A sailor never went to the windward of the captain, and he never failed to say, "Good morning," at his first appearance on deck.

When James went above, Mary went into the cabin to get her bonnet, then joined him on deck.

The men had lowered one of the boats and were sliding into it. James was getting ready to follow when he saw Mary. He hadn't noticed her best dress at breakfast, but when she came on deck wearing the gray bonnet he looked astonished.

"Where are you bound?" he asked with amusement in his voice.

"Ashore—with you," she said confidently.

"I had no notion of taking you ashore the first trip—not till I'd found out the lay of the land. But I don't know as it's safe to leave you here. You'd be taking a whaleboat and rowing yourself ashore, likely."

"Likely I would."

"Come along with you, then. Look alive there," he shouted to the men. "Swing that ladder over the side." Then gently, "Now, Mrs. Cleaveland." She's excited as a little girl, James thought. It would have been a shame to have left her.

James went down ahead of her, holding his arms above on the narrow rope ladder to protect her, but she climbed down lightly. "Many's the tree I've climbed down," she whispered. "This is easy."

As the boat approached the dock the sailors tossed their oars and were greeted in broken English by an official of the port. Was anybody sick? Any passengers to be landed? Any contraband goods? They took James's answers confidently. He arranged to allow his men shore leave, and then he walked with Mary along the crowded streets to the market place where they bought queer fruits and cheeses made of goat's milk.

But the pots of flowers made the greatest appeal of all to Mary. She bought some of the brightest ones in spite of James's protest that the cabin would be cluttered up and that they wouldn't grow with all the salt sea air coming in on them.

Mary reveled in the color, the warmth, the firmness of the land, walking along the crowded streets with James at her side followed by William West, the cabin boy, with an armload of purchases.

"Take these back to the shore, William, stow 'em in the boat under guard, and take the day off." Then turning to Mary, "Would you like to go up the hill to visit at the consulate?" And without waiting for an answer he called a small donkey-drawn conveyance, the only one in sight, helped her in, noticing with a stir of his pulse how she flushed with pleasure and smiled with her lips and her eyes and the dimple in her cheeks. This would be a nice cruise. He liked it himself.

36

THE whaling grounds! Somehow it was like any other part of the ocean, and yet Mary could almost see in every dark swell a whale's back and in each whitecap in the distance a leviathan breaking water. The usual lookouts were stationed in the rings at the masthead, but their watch was supplemented by a dozen pairs of eyes.

The captain nailed a gold piece to the mainmast, the nailheads clinching the dull yellow disk, so that each man could sharpen his eyes on it before he gazed out over the water. The *Seconet* would not be properly christened as a whaler until her decks were sloshed in oil and her sails and rigging were bathed in soot.

Mary knew that James was eager to make good with this fine new ship. The Cleaveland luck was a matter of excellent judgment and knowledge of the habits of whales, yet one could not catch them if there were no whales to be seen.

Day after day the tropical sun beat down on the watchers. Each night brought cool relief. A tenseness spread to the crew. The boys were "getting on edge." Given a sight of a whale now, there was every chance of getting him.

The boat steerers were spending more and more time on their gear and the already keen harpoons were honed to a still sharper edge. Line tubs were ready with the new line coiled "with the sun" in precise layers.

"There she blooooows!"

Mary was startled. This was the hail she had expected for days. Now she had almost ceased to listen for it. James was on the poop deck in an instant, shouting aloft for directions.

"Off the larboard bow, about three miles. A whole pod of 'em!"

James looked eagerly and Mary saw him grow tense. He gave a quiet order to the man at the wheel, and the *Seconet* changed her direction slightly. Most of the men were on deck and ready to go when the boats were lowered. All seemed quiet compared with the first drill she had seen on the way to Fayal.

Then Mary saw the whales. She must have been blind not to have seen them minutes ago. There were five or six of them close together and then a few more a long distance off. They were playing around. Occasionally one would sound, and his huge flukes would swing aloft as he slid beneath the surface.

"Mr. Look, stand by to heave her to."

The vessel slowed as the wind caught the other side of the mainsail and flattened it against the mast.

James was already in the rigging, halfway to the mast-head rings to relieve the lookout. Mr. Adams and Warren slid to the deck and ran to their boat.

The *Seconet* had hardly ceased moving when three of the whaleboats were in the water and the men in place at their oars. Mayhew Look's boat was steered down the wind with the third mate's boat close behind. Mr. Adams, the second mate, steered in between the large school and the few stragglers. Captain Cleaveland braced himself in the ring and shook his head. There was too much life in them and they were sure to be gallied. Still, Look's boat moved in on the pod until it seemed he must be ready to get his whale.

Mr. Look had made arrangements with his boat steerer to change places with him so that he could have the first chance to strike a whale. He now moved up into the bow as his boat steerer went back to the stern sweep.

Look waited a few minutes as the boat moved cautiously in. Then he rose, flexed his muscles, seized the iron, and heaved. The iron with its snaking line made a clear arc over the back of the whale and splashed into the water beyond. The captain was speechless with astonishment. With one accord, the whales sounded, and the ocean was once more bare.

"That ends it!" Captain Cleaveland muttered as he came down from the masthead.

James's anger was rising as the boats drew nearer. As they were hoisted in and secured, he stood and stared at his first mate; then he exploded, "Mr. Look, a whale's a big critter."

As the watch changed, there was talk about the gold piece.

"Take it, Warren, it's yours," said Adams. "You sighted the pod."

George Warren looked at the gold piece and a smile lighted up his dark face. "No, I guess I'll leave it be. We didn't have no luck, and I don't want to win no money on a lot of gallied whales."

Down in the forecastle, Isaac Reed said to him, "George Warren, ye've gone flared. Turnin' down a gold piece thet way."

Warren grinned and said, "I don't guess I'd 'a done it if it had been a plug of tobacco."

That noon Mr. Adams wrote in the logbook: "Commences with morderate breezes from N. by W. Saw gamb of whales. Lowered for them but to no purpose. Heading S. by E. Latter part the same. So ends."

The next day was hot and sultry. The *Seconet* cruised about with a sharp lookout on deck and aloft. The stage seemed to be set in just the same manner as the day before. Then came the hail. This time the ship was hove to sooner to prevent frightening the whales. The boats were hoisted and swung over, and as their crews slid down the falls Captain Cleaveland faced the first mate.

"Do something you've never done before, Mr. Look, and like enough you'll get a whale."

Mary saw the mate's expression. "James," she called in apprehension, but James was high in the rigging. Was he sending that nice young man to his death? She knew by the look on his face that he meant to get his whale or . . .

The alternative startled her. She thought of his little new wife, Elizy Ann, at home on the Vineyard.

The whales were quiet as the three boats moved in. Look changed places with his boat steerer once more. Mary steadied the glass against the deck housing. She saw him signal to the man at the steering oar and then she gripped the rail in excitement.

"Oh, oh! He's right on the whale's back!"

She saw the boat pitching up on a black mound while the mate heaved first one iron and then the second into the supporting flesh. There was a whirlpool of thrashing water, boat, and oars. At first she was sure that all had been wrecked. Then she saw the boat shoot out of harm's way and bob about like a lively cork. There was a great slick where the wounded whale had gone down.

"Look out! He'll come up under you!" shouted Captain Cleaveland from aloft, unmindful that his voice could not reach the boats, but the mate was in the right spot, instinctively it seemed, and as the whale rushed to the surface Look came alongside and used his lance. The whale thrashed in its death flurry and then turned fin out.

Mary looked for the other boats. Mr. Adams was fast to a whale and riding away from the ship. Mr. Howard's boat would help tow in the dead whale.

For several anxious hours the *Seconet* sailed, searching for the waist boat. A sharp lookout was kept from aloft. The huge carcass of the dead whale, chained alongside, strained and gurgled as the vessel moved forward.

It was a joyous moment when they sighted the bulk of the second whale, with the boat and crew standing by. A waif was flying from the back of the carcass and it

196

fluttered in the breeze. When the *Seconet* came within two or three cable's lengths, Captain Cleaveland gave orders to heave to.

When Mr. Adams and his boat's crew came aboard, George Warren went to the mainmast and pried out the gold piece from the encircling nailheads. This would be the forerunner of good whaling.

37

IT WAS weary labor, playing a whale, fighting to get a lance in at the life, and then towing the sluggish carcass back to the ship. But the difficulties had just commenced. The hard, dirty work of cutting in and trying out was ahead of them.

The first mate's whale was floating alongside with a heavy chain around the flukes. The second mate's catch was chained to the ship farther aft. The officers rigged up the cutting stage and went out on the narrow footboard.

The huge head was disjointed and hoisted to the level of the deck, where the first mate made an opening for bailing with "case buckets." The fine spermaceti went directly into special barrels without any trying. After they had salvaged all they could from the head, or "junk," it was dropped overboard, a feast for the sharks that were now swimming about.

They then cut into the body of the whale, chopping

through the thick blubber with long-handled cutting spades. Pulley blocks creaked as the tackle took up the weight of the huge slab of skin and fat that was being peeled from the whale. The great, flat iron hook strained in the tough skin as the thick blanket piece was hauled higher and higher toward the yards. As soon as the two blocks came together, a new hole was cut with a long boarding knife. Into this a new set of tackle was fixed with a heavy toggle, and strain was put on it. The upper part of the blanket piece was then cut loose with spades and swung in over the hatch to be lowered to the blubber deck and cut up into horse pieces.

The cutting in continued all through the night and well into the afternoon of the next day. The blubber room was filled up with horse pieces, and the men working there were covered with grease from head to foot. Even the smooth roll of the sea sent one of them sprawling on the slippery surface.

The scene that night was unforgettable. Flaming cressets lit up the deck and the cutting stage with flickering light as the mates slashed with their sharp spades. The pulley blocks creaked and the rigging groaned as the work went on.

The next afternoon saw the end of the cutting in, and men started the tryworks. They poured water into the trough so that the heat would not scorch the deck; then they brought wood and kindled the fire.

They tossed up the horse pieces through the hatch to the deck. A man was busy with the mincing knife, cutting slices in the fatty side through to the skin. "Bible leaves" they called them. They put these pieces into the trypot with long-handled forks to sizzle and try out like fat pork. The smoke did not thicken until the men started to feed the fire with the scraps. Then the greasy, black clouds rolled into the rigging and around the sails and hung over the deck like a pall. Mary could smell, feel, and taste it, and her clothes reeked with it so that she felt as if she would never again be clean.

As the night drew near, the scene became more and more memorable, until darkness made the dull red flames, the slipping and sliding men, and their service of the tryworks seem like some pagan rite. Aloft, the sails were set to keep the ship as nearly stationary as possible. The gleam of the fire, now bright, as fresh scraps were drawn from the melted mass and fed to the furnace, now dull, as the flames subsided, made the *Seconet* stand out like a beacon to be seen for miles.

Mary watched until late at night, fascinated by the scene. Once in a while during the next day she looked on with interest, until she was disgusted with the messy ship. The *Seconet* had been so pretty in her new, clean paint!

The next morning she stayed in bed late, not caring to see any more. At last she went on deck and to her surprise saw everything scoured clean. Except for a dinginess of the sails she would never have known that the *Seconet* was no longer "clean," that the ship had been baptized in oil, and that the Cleaveland luck was holding.

38

DAY after day the *Seconet* moved southward. It was the middle of January and the height of summer in the Southern Hemisphere, yet the nights were getting cooler. Mary went to her trunk for the woolen stockings and the afghan.

Now they were setting a course toward the southwest. "Off in the distance," one of the mates pointed out, "is Staten Island. It won't be long before we round the Horn."

The albatrosses joined them, and Mary never tired of watching these huge birds in their graceful flight. The sailors thought them stupid and were forever playing tricks on them. It was easy to catch them with hook and line, and when once on deck the birds were unable to fly away. Some of the men wanted to kill them for their down, but the older sailors said, "No, leave them be. It's bad luck to kill a gony." When they tired of the sport, they dropped the birds over the side. They rose to flight with little trouble when they felt the waves beneath their feet.

When Mary and James had rounded Cape Horn in the *Mary Wilder* they had come close enough to the high headlands so they could see the shore dimly. James told her he was heading farther south this time because the icebergs would not be dangerous now, and there was more sea room.

For several days they sailed through angry, gray seas with the cold wind lashing at them and no sign of warmth in the leaden sky. The ship beat first southwest and then northwest, always with double-reefed topsails. James was constantly on the alert for anything that might happen off this stormy cape. Mary didn't know when he slept. She'd wait at night to try to keep him company, but he'd send her off to bed.

One evening just at dusk James noticed a heavy bank of clouds to the south. He was disturbed and watchful. Mary, too, began to look at those clouds with apprehension. When darkness shut down there was something sinister out there. Suddenly there was a flash of lightning, and at the same instant Captain Cleaveland sprang into action.

"All hands on deck!" he shouted.

The men came tumbling up from the fo'castle. Mr. Adams ran to him, and Captain Cleaveland yelled against the rising gale, "Quick! Get all the canvas off her and stand by for a blow."

The men went into the rigging on the jump. As they snatched at the sails and fastened them in place, the wind continued to rise.

Men were now coming down out of the singing shrouds. Captain Cleaveland shouted, "Look alive there!" With a roar the gale was on them.

In the dim light, Mary could see the rigging steam with spray, and a sheet of water swept over the bulwarks and around her knees. She clung to the door at the head of the companionway as the *Seconet* went over farther and farther, until it seemed that she was hanging from the doorjamb. Then James grasped her and lowered her into the cabin.

"Are you all right?" he whispered anxiously. And without waiting for a reply he was back on the deck of his ship.

Mary groped about in the dark. Nothing would keep still. The sofa broke its lashings and followed Mary across the cabin. She staggered to the stateroom. As she tried to go through the narrow entrance with the mad thing after her, the ship plunged, knocking her head against the wall. She slumped into the wildly swaying bed and clung to it as the ship rolled and pitched. The *Seconet* was a tortured thing, but Mary's misery was limitless. All of the old seasickness and sea dread returned to her a hundredfold as she clung to the rails of the swaying bed. She said the prayers of her childhood, begging at the end for firm, dry land and quiet.

As she lay there it seemed that her poor, purged body finally found some of the peace for which she had prayed, and then she slept.

39

It was well over a month since the *Seconet* had rounded the Horn. To see the vessel now one would never suspect that she had been buffeted in the thundering gale from the Antarctic, for the sails had been mended and the broken spars and stove boats set in order.

They had cruised most of this time over the On Shore Whaling Grounds, which lay off the west coast of South America. There had been no further luck. The tally of oil still remained at 130 barrels.

The men looked at each other and out at the ocean.

"Why don't the old man go where the whales be?"

"Guess he would if he knew where they was."

"Why *don't* he know? That's his business. Why, when I went whalin' on the *Sea Bird*, some days we'd sight two-three whales to a time."

"Did you iron 'em all?"

"No." The lean sailor spit a large stream of tobacco

juice from the leeward side of his mouth. "But the old man knew where to go to look for 'em."

James heard this muttering and grumbling. He was used to feeling the tone of men's morale. He saw the more active boys getting impatient, comparing this with other voyages and infecting the youngest ones with their discontent.

"Got to get ashore for a spell, Mr. Look," he said.

"What! Now?"

"Yes, the boys need to stretch their legs."

"Well, we ain't far from Valparaíso," the mate said.

"Valparaíso be hanged! They charge too much for anchorage! And the city's too wild! All the young fellers we got here. It ain't fit for 'em. We'll head for Talcahuano, Chile, if it *is* two hundred or more miles further down the coast."

"We're more liable to meet other ships there, too," he added. "Vineyard ships headed home, like enough, and maybe we can transship what oil we've got here."

No one was more pleased than Mary to be able to go ashore. Each day she went on deck to see if the land wasn't taking on some more obvious form. Along toward the middle of March she noticed the greenness of the ocean and the immensity of it in the bright air. "We must be approaching land," she thought, "the ocean seems larger than ever, then."

James stood beside her. "We ought to be raising Point Arauco, soon, Mary. The pilot boats wait there, but I know the harbor well enough. I've been here a good many times as mate sailing with Captain Littlefield, or

Pa, and as captain of the *Mary Wilder*." Mary still stood by the deckhouse watching when James came back.

"Signal 'No pilot required,' Mr. Adams."

"Now there's a disappointed Irishman," James said.

"What's an Irishman doing here, James?"

"They're everywhere," James chuckled. "No, I tell you, Mary. Ever since the Chileans threw off the yoke of Spain they've been partial to the Irish on account of O'Higgins, who led them in their revolt. Most of the pilots in the harbor here are Irish."

"Maybe you'd better signal for one, then, or he'll get the best of you."

James would have put his arm around Mary if they had been in their cabin. As it was he smiled at her. "Ain't I safe from the Irish with you around to protect me?"

She smiled as James left her side to guide the ship into the harbor and then she smiled again at the beauty of the city snuggled beneath the towering mountains of the Andes.

The *Seconet* sailed through the passage behind the island of Quiriquina into the splendid harbor. They dropped anchor and paid out the cable until the vessel swung clear, then they furled the sails and made ready the captain's boat for the trip ashore.

Behind the protecting island the harbor lay, encircled by a crescent of shore line. There were no wharves, and the warehouses and other buildings were low adobe structures. Steep hills rose directly from the water, and the streets followed the contour of the harbor at the water front, but farther back formed rectangles. Mary found that they were anchored above what had formerly been part of the city. A violent earthquake and tidal wave had depressed the whole section and demolished the major part of the city of Talcahuano not many years before.

The captain took Mary ashore with him, and she was invited to stay at the consulate while James settled his affairs. She accepted eagerly, for she'd been long enough on board a whaler to appreciate the change. Perhaps she could gather roses from a sun-drenched patio. She had looked so long at the pathetic little bunch of artificial flowers that she'd bought in Fayal and stuck jauntily in the cabin mirror. As James had predicted, her plants had been blighted by the sea.

40

AFTER a short stay at Talcahuano they headed straight for the Off Shore Grounds, several hundred miles to the westward, for the whaling had been poor nearer the coast. The *Seconet* wallowed in the sea with topsails set. In case of a blow the sails would be reefed, but other than this there was little for the men to do but stand their watches.

The men would sit in the shade of the deckhouse, talking and whittling. James frowned at the whittling. He couldn't tolerate unproductive work, but he didn't like to stop it because it occupied the men's minds and kept them out of mischief.

"They're used to a stacked-up woodpile," he complained to Mary, "and they can't see that we need every stick of wood for the galley stove. The worst of it is that they never make anything." And to the men, finally, "You act like a lot of farmers, settin' there whittlin'!"

That was disgrace enough for a sailor. One and all they turned to the scrimshaw work. James had the ship's carpenter saw off chunks of the jawbone and portioned it out to the men.

Some of them made beautiful things of it—jagging wheels, vases, bodkins—all useful—even swifts, so that their mothers or sweethearts could wind worsted as the contrivance turned. One of the sailors made a swift with each small piece jointed so that it folded into a little box not more than a foot long, then spread out gracefully when opened.

Edwin Williams made Mary a jagging wheel carved from whalebone and decorated with India ink. Mary hoped that she hadn't lost the faculty for making pies that she had learned so painstakingly from Caroline Luce.

For weeks they sailed. Mary felt that it was an aimless existence, cruising back and forth, with little change except at the infrequent tacks. But when James pointed out the evidences of whales' feeding grounds—mangled fragments of octopus—and explained some of their habits, she realized that the seemingly aimless wandering was a well-thought-out campaign, as cleverly played as a chess game.

Time dragged! Mary tried to sew, but the motion of the ship jerked her needle and made her prick her fingers. She tried to read, but the print blurred before her eyes. Though she had been a poor sailor, she had known pleasant hours when the weather was calm, when she had enjoyed the warm sun and soft breeze. Now she began to feel sick almost continually. When she awoke in the morning her head ached, and even in a calm sea the slightest motion of the ship brought on spasms of nausea. She tried to get up and go about as though nothing were wrong, for it was unbelievable that she could be seasick in such fine weather.

However ill she felt, she never ceased to thrill as the call "Bloooows!" came from the masthead. She would go to the deck to look eagerly for the breaching whales miles away, to watch James as he ordered the boats' crews to "Hoist and swing! Lower away!"

She stood by the rail as the boats swept down on the unsuspecting animals, sometimes with sails set, white triangles in the sun, sometimes with oars dipping, dipping, dipping. She watched the iron strike. With her clear vision she could sometimes see the men pouring sea water on the loggerhead to keep it from scorching as the whale sounded with the line. She watched lest a boat be taken beyond reach of the ship in encircling mist or darkness. She knew in just which direction each boat had gone. When the boats returned she would go to her cabin, tired and sick, wanting only to be let alone.

The excitement held over and was with her continually. Then it occurred to her why she had been sick each morning, why her head ached, and why her stomach rebelled, for she had heard in Caroline Luce's homely language that one of these days she'd be due for it. She was going to have a baby.

James found her crying when he came into the cabin, tired from contending with cutting in the blubber.

"What's the matter now?" he asked testily.

"James, I believe we're going to have a baby."

"H'm, that's nothing to cry about."

"But I feel sick all the time."

James went over to her, touched her hand and her hair.

"We'll be making port soon," he said.

It was many weeks, however, before they did.

41

Now they were off the coast of Peru, headed toward Paita. They had been away from land for five months and had taken about 250 barrels more of oil—not very good luck, but a steady rise.

James recalled how, when he was mate on the *Hopewell* near these shores, Captain Littlefield had beaten back and forth off Cape Blanco for five days and finally had given up trying to make Paita. James wouldn't have given up if he'd been headed for port—not then—but he found as he grew older that it was sometimes best to modify your notions. The sea was a great one for taking a man down if he began to think his own ideas were too important.

To Mary the shore line near Cape Blanco was a scene of utter desolation. She could see nothing green—just bare hills and shore that looked like a slag heap.

On August 13 they made the port of Paita and dropped

anchor in a fine natural harbor, a place so well protected that ships were never troubled by storms. Mary went ashore with James, glad to set foot on land no matter how bleak and dreary.

As the boat pulled up to the small pier, things took on individual form. The narrow streets and low adobe houses shimmered with rainbow hues in the hot, dry air.

The United States consul, Fayette M. Ringgold, and his Spanish wife, Alvida, gave them a warm welcome. Consul Ringgold was a champion of seamen's rights and fought a bitter and relentless war on the land sharks and unprincipled whalers with whom he came in contact. He admired all the more upright men like James, who wouldn't stoop to cheating sailors.

Alvida took Mary into her confidence, for she, too, was expecting a baby. They talked over the necessities for infants.

Mary had made a little dress from one of James's handkerchiefs, which she exhibited proudly.

"What a dear little shirt!" Alvida exclaimed.

"It's a dress," said Mary.

But it did not conform to Alvida Ringgold's standards for infant garments, with long skirts and ruffles. She gave Mary a great many new ideas and patterns and above all a feeling of confidence in the kinship of all women.

Mary bought some soft, hand-woven material. She could do a lot of sewing in four months, and her baby would be well outfitted.

Now, when she went back to the ship, she worked in

earnest on little garments while the *Seconet* cruised on the On Shore Grounds.

"I'll work down the coast to Talcahuano and put you ashore there," James told Mary.

"Couldn't I have the baby there at Paita? I like Alvida Ringgold—and she's going to have one, too." Mary whispered the last few words that had been told her in confidence. Surely she could tell it now.

"That so?"

"Yes, just about the same time."

"Pretty hot there in December, Mary. She's used to it, but you're not."

"Yes, I suppose it would be." She knew that when the wind blew the dry dust about it would be worse than a Sydney brickfielder, when small particles of red sand descended. At the thought of it she was seized with nostalgia. Strange how people long for even the discomforts of their early childhood!

"There's a fine doctor there, too. Well known throughout the whaling fleet. He cured Captain Russell of a bad case of scurvy."

Back and forth they cruised along the coast, right through the On Shore Grounds, looking in vain for whales. At the full of the moon the watch was redoubled, for old whalers said the critters appeared then, stayed for a week or so, then vanished. James didn't take much stock in those tales. Still he wouldn't take any chances.

Mary felt more and more uncomfortable as the days passed, but she wouldn't complain lest she interfere with the business on hand. James was so intent on whaling that all else seemed to have gone from his mind.

One evening, however, she approached him timidly, "James, don't you think we had better go to Talcahuano, where they have a doctor?"

"We're headed for port right now," he told her, "but I'll set more sail if you say so. The child will be born under the American flag, either here or at the consulate, but I don't want the job on my hands."

Sea captains often had to act as doctors. James told her of a Captain Coffin from Nantucket who was badly injured by a whale. He realized that his leg would have to be amputated, so he called his mate and with gun in hand said, "Now, you've got to cut off my leg. If you flinch, I'll shoot." He propped himself up and gave directions about handling each artery and vein. When the job was done, and not until then, they both keeled over.

"It wouldn't be the first time I've acted as doctor, but I've never taken the role of midwife. We'll make all sail for Talcahuano."

42

AT TALCAHUANO Mary couldn't lie still. She couldn't sit up. James told her she was like the man at the Vineyard who said, "I've et so many cowcumbers I can neither lay nor set." She laughed and tried to control herself, but her legs twitched, her back ached, and her head felt heavy. Neither Caroline Luce nor young Eliza Cleaveland had been so sick when their babies were coming. She began to fear some abnormality.

James looked at her uncomprehendingly. "Seems as if you feel most as bad on land as you did at sea. I thought you'd feel all right as soon as you touched port."

Mary didn't answer. She took James's hand and laid it against her warm abdomen.

"Say! The little devil kicks." And James felt a new kindship with the child who was part his flesh and blood and part Mary's.

"Tomorrow they come for you?" Mary asked.

"Yes. The *Seconet* will stand off and on, and they'll send the ship's boat in."

"Couldn't you stay, James? Couldn't you stay until it's over?"

"Why, Mary, likely 'twill be a month. I got here as quick as I could because I didn't want to take any chances of having the child born without a good doctor."

"It's coming soon, James, I'm sure."

"There's no telling how long. And what good would I be? It's nothing to be afraid of. Every woman that's any account has to go through it."

"All alone?"

"Why, there's folks here. Mrs. Crosby and the servants and the doctor."

"But I want you, James, to hold my hand."

"I'd only get in the way. And what should I say to the agents if they asked, 'Where were you, and why weren't you whaling?'"

"Tell them . . . " Well, James had made up his mind that his duty lay on shipboard. She shouldn't try to dissuade him. She was glad he was not a shallow man, easily influenced. She swallowed the big lump in her throat and smiled. "I'll make out, James."

"Now, that's more like the plucky girl I married. I'll go now and make all arrangements."

When James returned he told her everything was ready. "I left $500 in gold with the consul. That should take care of you for a year if necessary, with the baby paid for in advance. I didn't see the doctor, but they say he's a clever chap—an Englishman. Here's some fruit for you." James emptied his pockets. "New kinds. I'll

2 1 7

wager you've never seen the like before—unless you had them in Australia."

The words brought on a touch of homesickness, a vision of her mother. If only her mother could stand by her as she had stood by Cecily. If only she could get a letter from her mother!

The next day the *Seconet's* boat picked up the captain.

"Are you all right?" he asked as he left.

"To be sure," she answered gaily, with the Irish lilt he loved. "And next time you come ashore I'll show you something."

She knew this ordeal was one she must face alone. James must go whaling. He had been with her here only one night, now he would be gone. She thought of the time she had parted from him on the wharf at Holmes's Hole. What a child she had been! She wouldn't go down to the ship with him now. No, ladies stayed under cover at a time like this. And besides, she didn't want to see him sail away.

43

CHRISTMAS time! The noise and confusion in the streets was hilarious. There had been feasting for several days. Girls dressed in holiday clothes with flowers in their dark hair paraded along before the Plaza, arm in arm with gaily dressed young men. Mary loved the laughter and the brightness and wished she, too, might go out on the arm of her escort, instead of being confined with this ugly body, listening to Mrs. Crosby's comments on the immorality of modern youth.

"No, my dear, I've had too much experience with holiday celebrations. Drunken and disorderly sailors come into the compound and have to be taken care of. I try to get away from it all by shutting and barring the windows and going to the rear of the building."

It was obvious there would be no celebration here to make Mary forget her loneliness, her longing for home, her desire to see James. It seemed to cause a dull heaviness to hang on her.

Last Christmas she was determined that she should do something to make the day different, even though they were rounding the Horn. She thought so far ahead that while they were in Fayal she bought a little bottle of wine, and she put it on the table as she and James sat down. But James wouldn't have it opened.

"No," he said. "I can't say to the men, 'No drinking,' and then come in here and swill down liquor. No, Mary. Put it in the medicine chest, and then whoever needs it, officer or man, shall have some. It's a nice present for the ship. I thank you."

And so the only difference was that Mary wore her low-necked silk gown and presided over the officers' table with extra dignity. And James was as expansive as though he were serving champagne.

What a strange, grinding sort of pain! Had she eaten something to disagree with her? She must be more careful of her diet, now.

The sounds of the Christmas festivities attracted her attention once more. What a jolly season it had always been at home. Father and the boys invariably drank too much punch, but it never made them ugly as the stuff they bought at the Golden Bar sometimes did. It was one of the times Mother was indulgent and let them have their punch at home.

Mother began weeks beforehand by making suet pudding with plums and citron in it and putting it away to season. And each one made some gift amidst great secrecy.

Then on Christmas Day Mother cooked a joint of

mutton or a piece of beef with Yorkshire pudding. There was always something special if she had to save for weeks.

When she was little, what a gay time Father had made of it! He'd tell them stories on Christmas Eve—beautiful stories of snow-covered fir trees and English holly, always finishing with some fanciful tale of old Ireland and wonderful things that the fairies accomplished.

That pain again!

"Mrs. Crosby! Mrs. Crosby!"

"There! All the excitement of this holiday has brought your time of confinement ahead! I'll send for Mr. Crosby!" Mrs. Crosby sent maids scurrying hither and yon to find her husband, to ask him to send for the doctor.

The pains grew more severe; a grinding sensation came every half hour. Nightfall drew near without relief. Where was the doctor? Another messenger was sent, but he came back to say the doctor was away.

"Away!" said Mrs. Crosby scornfully. "He's drunk!"

"Oh, what shall I do?" cried Mary. Eaton was the only doctor in town.

The pains came more frequently. Mary paced up and down in agony and tried to stifle the cries of suffering, the groans that were wrung from her involuntarily.

"Oh, I can't stand this any longer," said Mrs. Crosby, wringing her hands. "Stay with her, Concita! She needs you more than I do. I'll do without you tonight," she said in Spanish.

Now there was no one—no one but Concita, who could speak only Spanish. But Concita had a solution. There was an old midwife down near the docks. She had brought many a baby into the world. She tried to tell Mary, but Mary couldn't understand. Finally she nodded—anything—she'd accept anything that would help. But when Concita started to go, Mary held her.

"No, no. Don't leave me!"

The woman smiled. "No. I no go." She opened the door and called, "Anita," and sent the girl scurrying for the old Chilean woman.

As the door opened Mary heard ribald laughter and singing from the men who had been picked up as deserters and detained by the consul.

"When, oh, when, will this be over?" Mary asked herself. She *must* wait until the doctor came. But she couldn't live through another hour of this.

"Poor James!" thought Mary, "he'll feel badly when he comes back, and finds me d-dead." But her thoughts of James's future were cut short by present pain.

Concita led her silently to the bed, and, pointing to the door, "She comes," the girl said.

Mary looked up, feeling that her agony would now be over, only to see a wrinkled, bent old hag, fumbling around in a dirty satchel, muttering incantations in a foreign tongue. She screamed at the thought of having this repulsive creature touch her. Then the door opened and in staggered the English doctor—drunk.

Overpowering waves of pain obscured the details, but Mary realized that the need for action had sobered the doctor, that he was working over her quietly, kindly. She struggled on through the rest of the night, through the morning, and finally sank back exhausted.

When she awoke she felt numb and for a time could

222

not remember what had happened. Then she made out a silent figure by the bed. Concita, in a fresh white apron, was holding up the little girl that was her baby and James's.

She was glad it was a girl, though she had really wanted a boy for James's sake. He wanted a man child to be a sea captain like his fathers before him.

Mary slept intermittently, but as the night drew on she became more aware of her pain-wracked body and of her sordid surroundings. There were fights nearby, vile cursing. Then the climax came when she realized that on the other side of the court was a man in delirium. She could hear his ravings terminated at length by a pistol shot. She found out later that he had committed suicide.

The whole of the following week would remain forever as a nightmare, and Mary wondered how she had survived with her little new daughter.

It was several weeks before Mary was able to get up. The men from the compound had been taken by a ship that was shorthanded. Some hardy captain had looked over the ill-favored lot and had said with grim pride, "I can handle 'em." The stir caused by the suicide in the next room had subsided. Everything was serene, yet Mary could never enter the room without a shudder. Mrs. Crosby had another room prepared in the other end of the long rambling structure where it was pleasanter. Here she could look out toward the ocean.

A native woman, cleaner than most, was hired to take care of the baby girl, and Mary had more freedom. She was urged to take walks to regain her strength, but no prospect pleased her. The town was drab, with only occasional spots of garden. Beyond the hills the whole earth was dry and brown. There was no incentive for one who was used to rambling in beautiful fields and woods.

One day she discovered a pretty little place beside one of the streams that emptied into the harbor. It was cool and fragrant early in the morning. A clear stream, set deep between the banks, gurgled down from pool to pool. Green leaves and bright flowers made the spot a fairyland. Talcahuano might be thousands of miles away.

Sometimes the native women came with baskets of washing on their heads, and in a short time there would be a whacking of paddles against the sodden clothes and a clatter of unmusical voices.

Mary felt better each day. As her strength returned, she longed for the *Seconet* and all its associations. She wanted to be with James. She missed the young Vineyard sailors with their courteous indifference to her. She missed her own bed on the ship.

One day in March, Mr. Crosby came to Mary with a smile, and said, "Good news for you, Mrs. Cleaveland. We have sighted a vessel entering the harbor that looks like the *Seconet*."

Mary hastily threw a scarf over her hair and went with Mr. Crosby. It was indeed the *Seconet*. What a beautiful sight it was to see her move slowly to the anchorage. The sails looked a little dingier. Perhaps that meant more oil.

She watched as the boat was lowered. She recognized James at the steering oar, looking handsomer even than when she had first seen him in Honolulu.

Mary rushed up to him, and he embraced her right before all the others. She thought his first question would be about the baby, but no! He looked into her eyes and saw that she was well. He took her arm possessively in his, and together they walked to the customhouse, where he registered his ship and 60 more barrels of oil. Then they turned to go and see the baby.

"It's a girl," Mary said half apologetically.

James soon fell in love with his daughter. No other child could ever supplant her in his heart. His first baby, with blue eyes and fair hair. Unquestionably she looked like the Cleavelands. She even had a little down-turned mouth, which looked adorable on a baby.

"What shall we call her?" James knew Mary wouldn't name the baby before he came. He suggested "Mary," but the young mother shook her head and still called her child "Niñita," one of the few Spanish words she had cared to adopt.

44

IT WAS good to be back on the *Seconet*, in her own cabin
with its familiar pictures. The little girl was in a big,
flat basket that could be put under the bed when not in
use. In calm evenings Mary took the baby out on deck,
rocking her in her arms and singing. The mates and
sailors went by softly. Mayhew Look thought of Elizy
Ann at home in West Tisbury. Charles Adams had a girl
at home, too. When she first came aboard the sailors had
asked to see the baby and had stood before her with caps
in hand.

They cruised along the On Shore Grounds up to
Paita, where they stopped for a day. Mary found that
Alvida had a baby girl, Mercedes.

In October they put into Tumbes, where James bought
wood for a little crib. He would have it fashioned like a
regular bed, with one side free to fit against their own
and a little low railing that would snuggle against the

side of the cabin. They could lash on a piece of canvas for the bottom. This wood that grew in the jungle was very hard and lasting.

"'Twill do for the next one, too," said James with a chuckle.

When the baby was nearly a year old they stopped at the Galápagos Islands.

The *Seconet* rolled slightly in the swell as she swung at anchor. The equatorial sun beat down in all its ardor on the hot pine planking, but a slight breeze was blowing.

The captain's boat and two others had gone ashore to get tortoise. Even now Mary could see one of the foraging parties toiling down the steep rock slopes of the island with a heavy burden to put in one of the whale-boats. The men worked with a will because they had visions of fresh meat, turtle soup, and steaks. The creatures would roam around the deck for a long time, causing no trouble at all.

The islands swarmed with huge tortoise that laid their eggs and made their headquarters there. Anyone with enough ambition to climb to the plateau could easily turn over the great reptiles, then all that remained was to get them to the ship. They ate little or nothing, did not need a great deal of care, and furnished meat that would be the envy of an epicure. The shell, too, was another bit of material for the men to scrimshaw.

The tortoise caught by the boats' crews were not the largest. Some of the big ones would tax the huskiest crews to freight them to the ship. Those they took measured a foot or two across. The captain kept two of the largest "to take home to Father." Each time the older whalers would land, they'd search for some of the patriarchs and, if lucky, would add another date to the many carved in the horny shells.

The islands were named after the tortoise—galapago was the Spanish name, and good fortune placed them in one of the whaling grounds. James had said there would be little whaling there this season and planned to set out for the Mid Pacific Grounds as soon as they had the tortoise and fresh water aboard and had looked over the mailbox.

They carried several letters ashore, and put them into the old barrel that some ingenious whaler had nailed to a pole.

"Could they possibly reach a vessel going to Australia?" Mary had asked.

"Very likely."

So she wrote to her mother, laboriously, for spelling was a task. She managed to pen a glowing account of James and their little daughter, born at the American consulate in Talcahuano, Chile.

The baby would soon be running everywhere. Even now she could walk around, holding things, rushing headlong from one person to the next. She was friendly to the sailors, and they told her stories as though she could understand them. They fashioned toys for her. One of them made her a whalebone teething ring, and another, a ring for her napkin.

After the boats' crews had returned they weighed anchor and the *Seconet* headed for the grounds. They kept a sharp lookout all of the time because there might be whales in these waters. James sighed for the good old days when it was not uncommon to sight dozens in a day. He recalled the excitement back in 1847, on that busy Sunday in October.

The *Hopewell* had run into a pod of sperm whales. He had charge of the waist boat, as second mate. First the larboard boat struck a whale, and while she was busy keeping out of the way of whale and sizzling line he steered his boat into the smother. A huge black shape washed up just under him and he let go with his iron just as he saw the spiracle coming out of the water. Then there was trouble. He found that he and Mr. Wells of the larboard boat were fast to the same whale. James had a hazy recollection of a mass of tangled line and then his own line smoking over the loggerhead. He heard Mr. Wells shout, "You hold him. My iron drawed out." In a few minutes he caught a glimpse of the larboard boat fast to another. Before he had finished he had two whales waifed, ready for the ship, Mr. Wells had another pair, and Mr. Esterbrook one more. That was real whaling.

He had enjoyed himself on the old *Hopewell*, with his carefree life and no real responsibility but that of a second mate.

In the next four months they were to get only two more whales. They now had 760 barrels of oil. The luck, though not good, was better than that of others. Captain Soule of the *Milo* reported that he had sailed around New Zealand and "didn't get a horse piece." Whale ships cruised and cruised. The men grew restless, and soon most of the captains had more to worry about than catching whales. Captain Cleaveland noticed the discouragement among his crew and decided to put in to

Talcahuano for wood and water and to give his men a chance to stretch their legs ashore. It would take their minds off the scarcity of oil and the small amount each man would receive as his "lay."

As Mary looked at the port in the distance, she said to herself, "A hateful-looking place!" But she really didn't mean it, for it was beautiful, lying there at the water's edge, snuggled under the mountains. Her first thought on seeing it once more was of the misery she had suffered there—but she had found happiness, too. She was always glad to go ashore, and she wanted to show the baby to the friends she had made at the consulate.

This stop of two weeks at Talcahuano was a fortunate one, for there James found Mr. Washburn, a nice young man from New York state, who had been with him as boat steerer on his last voyage on the *Mary Wilder*. He had been third mate on the ship *Leonidas* and had been put ashore there because of a temporary illness. James shipped him gladly as fourth mate. He also signed up Mr. Brown, of the ship *Columbia*, as third mate to replace Mr. Howard, who transferred to another ship.

Mr. Washburn was unassuming and mild, yet he had dignity. The baby liked him. She would climb upon his knee and laugh and coo whenever he had leisure to play with her. One day she rushed to his defense when he and one of the other officers were having a wrestling match. After that the sailors often teased her. They liked to see the little girl step in, crying, "Don't hurt Mitter Wap-Wap!"

"She looks just like the old man!" they'd say.

Mary was glad of the opportunity the town afforded

to improve the baby's diet. Before reaching port she had made broth of the turtle meat and the few foods at her disposal. At Talcahuano the baby had plenty of milk.

"James," she said, "I wish we had a little cow aboard."

"Where'd we put her fodder, I'd like to know?" was James's only answer.

A few days later, however, he told Mary that they were headed for the island of Juan Fernández to get a goat for the baby.

The island was not a great distance from Talcahuano, so the *Seconet* soon made a sheltered bay to the north of the rocky shore. There the boat was lowered and Captain Cleaveland landed with Mary and the baby. The *Seconet* sailed "off and on" waiting for him to return.

As they approached the shore, Mary could see the fernlike foliage and get faint odors of sandalwood. Alexander Selkirk spent four years of voluntary exile amongst its rocky hills and caves, furnishing Defoe with his inspiration for *Robinson Crusoe*. Mary recalled reading of the wild goats he had tamed, and she wondered if James would buy a descendant of one of Crusoe's little companions.

They had trouble making a landing, for the surf pounded on the rocky shore. Several men, Chileans from the settlement on the island, waded in and helped them land in a sheltered cove.

The little house where they stopped was occupied by a withered old woman, who shared it with a small herd of goats. Mary and James, with the help of the baby, had no difficulty in making her understand their needs. The old woman brought out a gourd, milked the goat into it, and gave the child some of the milk from a wooden spoon. The baby drank it eagerly, saying, "More, more."

The old woman laughed, and Mary did too. One of her problems was solved.

James put his hand on one of the goats, a velvety-eyed little white one with black spots, and asked for milk from that one. They tasted it and found it creamy and good. Then James took a gold coin from his pocketbook and put it down. "Will that pay for the goat?" he shouted. The woman understood and was delighted. She had plenty of goats. If necessary she could tame more from the wild herds on the mountains. Never before had she seen so much gold. She thought of the things she would be able to buy—calico, dishes—why, if she wanted to she could almost buy a new house.

Mary thought it was gold well spent. Here was health-giving food for the baby.

James turned the goat over to a sailor. "Find out how to handle this concern," he said.

James bought more vegetables, too. He had already stocked the ship at Talcahuano, but he never could get enough green things. He hated the diet of salt meat and hard tack which most of the whalers used so freely.

When their mission was accomplished, they walked along with the baby riding James's shoulder. They went down the trail to the cave where Selkirk was supposed to have lived. There was a wild beauty to the island with its treelike ferns and its volcanic cone.

All too soon they made their way back to the boat and left the island. They pulled out towards the distant ship, and the *Seconet* altered her course to bear down and pick them up. Mary would be glad to get the little thing safely aboard ship. To have fresh milk for the baby seemed too good to be true.

The goat, however, was destined to cause trouble. They had difficulty in getting her aboard at first. James laughed at himself and the crew for making such a time about the frightened little animal when they could handle a whale as a matter of course. They finally put slings under her and got her to the deck. Then they brought aboard large baskets and bundles of fodder, for Captain Cleaveland wouldn't have an animal around without plenty of food for it.

"Why, goats will eat anything, Captain," Mr. Look said.

James knew better. They were particular creatures. This one turned out to be especially so. She'd act fussy if her food came in contact with the oil casks. "The plaguey critter turns up her nose if you even breathe on her food," the sailors said.

Years later, when the little girl picked at her food, James insisted she had taken her daintiness from the goat.

45

AGAIN the sea seemed more than Mary could bear. She felt sick each morning, and the gentle rocking of the ship on a calm sea upset her. Even the little girl could not shake her from the lethargy that seemed to have fallen on her. Even with James's arms about her in their cabin she felt dull and unresponsive. Her eyes looked sunken and her cheeks pale. James noticed that she was not well.

"I'll put you ashore at Paita," he said finally. "Then I'll cruise on the Off Shore Grounds. I shan't likely be gone more'n six months."

Six months! It would seem like an eternity. She remembered that she had watched James go from the port of Holmes's Hole to be gone two years, leaving her alone among his people. A chill shook her as she thought of it. And here, too, she would be among strangers. Well, she'd get along. Anything but the roll and pitch and movement of the ship, the noise of the sails and the hum of the rigging, the smell of whale oil or greasy smoke. Even the odor of coffee as she passed the galley made her sick. She must get her feet on land!

In Paita things seemed little better at first. Her bed in the consulate seemed to ride and toss each night. Her walk on the smooth floor was unsteady. She couldn't eat. She could scarcely sit at the table long enough for the little girl to finish her breakfast.

It was then that Captain DeBlois's wife took charge. She was older than Mary—a large, calm, motherly woman. It was one of the sorrows of her life that she had no children. She put her arms around Mary. "Let me take care of you, dear. You ought to go to bed until you feel better." Mary started to protest. "I'll take care of Niñita, too."

So Mary rested in the quiet room at the consulate. The consul and Mrs. Ringgold sent up fruit and all sorts of special delicacies. Mrs. DeBlois brought in the little girl each day and stayed to talk with Mary. Alvida Ringgold, the young Spanish wife of the American consul, came with little Mercedes, and each day Alvida's old nurse took the two children out for a drive.

As Mary grew stronger she realized how seriously ill she had been, and that the care she had been given at this period had perhaps saved her life. The color came back to her cheeks. Her eyes were bright and her speech witty, with the Irish twist to her words.

"Ah! A good thing it is to be about on my feet again."

Mrs. DeBlois helped her into the long, full skirt she had worn and gave her a silk jacket of her own that fell in loose folds.

2 3 5

Tonight she'd go down to dinner, the first time in nearly a month. She'd go down early to be company for the children at their supper.

And they needed company, she found, for the children, Mercedes and Niñita, began hitting their cereal-covered spoons against the table, swearing great oaths at each other. Mary couldn't understand them, but she knew the import of their words, and she realized that they had been fascinated by the language of the Peruvian mule drivers, and had found it easy and effective to imitate them.

Alvida came running at the sound and shook little Mercedes.

"Naughty child! Never, never say such talk again."

"It's time I was up and about, to be sure," Mary thought. "James Cleaveland's child swearing like a muleteer!" She began to laugh. She couldn't help it, it seemed so incongruous. All the while she had been on the *Seconet* among the sailors she had never heard an oath.

She stopped laughing suddenly and became very serious. "No, no, dear. Talk nicely, like a little lady. See! Pret-ty flow-er."

"Pwetty f-ower," the little girl repeated and added of her own accord, "Pwetty mama."

Mary blushed, for just then she saw a handsome young man standing in the doorway and knew that he had heard it, too. Niñita saw him at the same moment, pushed her chair away from the table, turned around backward like a sailor coming down a rope ladder, quickly reached the floor, and tottered over to the doorway, calling, "Len, Len! Mama, see Len!"

Mary rose and made a curtsy. "When I am ill my

236

XXXXXXXXXXXXXXXXXX

ALVIDA RINGGOLD
CLEAVELAND

XXXXXXXXXXXXXXXXXX

XXXXXXXXXXXXXXXXXX

MERCEDES
RINGGOLD

XXXXXXXXXXXXXXXXXX

daughter takes advantage of me and flirts with young men!" Mary said in mock disapproval.

In answer Len said very little, for he was surprised to see a woman so young and beautiful and full of life, with a voice that made him feel queer inside as though he were hearing some exquisite music.

46

AFTER that Mary and Len Sanford, the young secretary, were often together. She liked to talk to him. Niñita would seek every occasion to chase after him, and Mary would have to follow her. Then he'd pick up the little girl and walk along with her on his shoulder, talking in the most natural way.

"I'm glad you happened to be here in Paita," Mary told him.

"I came near being in irons instead."

Mary laughed. Such a nice young man being treated like a criminal!

"I mean it."

And Mary saw that he was serious. So she listened while he told her what he had told no one else except Consul Ringgold.

He had been born in New York state of an old, proud family, but adventure called him. He wanted to leave, to be on his own entirely. He decided he'd go to sea.

"Why is it," Mary asked, "that boys always want to go to sea?"

"I could have told you then. I can't now. There was a certain Captain Cushman who used to come to Father's, and I asked him for a job. He gave me a berth as sailor.

"I was a greenhorn for fair. I didn't know a halyard from the painter. I hardly knew the foretopsail from a jib. But I learned the best I could and tried to do my part without shirking. But I couldn't seem to do anything right for the mate, a Mr. Fisher. I tried, and then I got over trying when I found 'twas no use. He'd go to the captain and complain, but the captain knew my father, and he knew I meant well, so, although he never exactly sided with me, he gave the mate to understand that perhaps he was somewhat to blame himself.

"Things might have worked out, but the captain got sick and died. Then when Fisher took command I was in for it. He was a petty man and couldn't run the ship without friction, so he gave us plenty of that. Some sailor took more water than his share, so he had him flogged. Another was strung up to the yardarm for some small infringement of rules. The hold was dirty and crawling with rats and insects, and the food would turn your stomach."

Mary thought of the clean quarters on the *Seconet*, where, except for homesickness, the chief complaint was the sameness of diet. And even that James was constantly striving to change.

"The sailors would get together in the hold and curse

and grumble, and then old Gumshoe Manning would come into our quarters with a lash and switch us all out. I was ready to rebel, but I knew it wouldn't get me anywhere, or any of the others; so I kept still, hoping to escape.

"Then a Portuguese boat steerer started a half-baked sort of mutiny. I refused to join him, but when it was quelled Fisher blamed me.

"By the time the *Lancer* reached Paita last May I had served all but three months of my time. I suppose the old boy wanted to get rid of me so I'd forfeit my pay. He succeeded. Pay didn't mean a thing to me compared to being free from that ship. And I've had enough of whaling, too."

"They're not all like that," Mary said.

"I'm not looking any further. If it hadn't been for Consul Ringgold I'd have been in jail. But he sized up the situation and couldn't seem to find me until after the *Lancer* had left port."

"Captain Cleaveland says the treatment in this port is always fair."

"Ringgold is a fine man, I can tell you. I was given a job as secretary at Callao, then early this year I was transferred back here. I like the service and would like to be able to go on with Ringgold's work in advocating fairer laws for sailors."

"If men only realized that ships *can* be run without cruelty, without dirt and hunger! I *know*, from observation, that they can be!"

"But Captain Cleaveland doesn't make as much profit as some of the others. There's the rub."

2 4 0

Yes, there was the rub. And Mary realized then that if ships were scarce, some other man who could save more money would be given command of the *Seconet*.

Not long after this a ship came to port with the consular correspondence from Washington, including an official document for Len Sanford, which notified him of his appointment to be consul at Tumbes. It was signed by President Buchanan and approved by the United States Senate.

"Len, I'm so glad for you!" Mary said.

"Leaving as consul is quite different from my arrival, when I sneaked up into a cabin in the mountains to hide and came down here penniless and desperate."

47

THE last day of September the new baby was born—a fat, healthy girl. Henrietta DeBlois stood by, and Alvida Ringgold. It hadn't been a difficult birth compared with the first one, and Mary recovered quickly with the excellent care and friendly company. Everyone at the consulate loved the new baby, and Niñita proudly brought her friends to see her little sister.

As Mary's strength returned she rambled through the streets of Paita to the old cemetery and to the Catholic church. The service reminded her of her early days at Saint Patrick's in Sydney. She thought of the prim little church on Martha's Vineyard. It might be several years before they got back. She wondered if James would consider having the children christened here, brought up as he was to despise Catholicism.

She kept thinking it over as the women sat sewing, looking out toward the Pacific to watch for familiar vessels.

During the first part of November the harbor of Paita began to fill with whaling ships. Some had just arrived from the Galápagos, but most of them had come in from the Off Shore Grounds. The crews were busy getting wood and water and provisions for the next cruise, or transshipping casks of oil to vessels that were homeward bound.

"I'm always relieved when I see the ships," Henrietta said. "I've never felt the same since the *Ann Alexander* was sunk by a whale." And she told the story as she had heard it from her husband who had been the captain.

Mary recalled the time she had first heard the story, when this captain's name had meant nothing to her. James had told it to her as they were sitting on the west step at home in the twilight.

On the thirteenth several more ships came in.

"Look! There's the *Mary Wilder!*" How it brought back those days at Honolulu! Clear, blue skies and soft, warm air—and James! There was the *Niger*, sailed by an Edgartown man, and Captain Stanton's ship, the *Osprey*. Perhaps there'd be news—from the Vineyard, from San Francisco, from Sydney. Perhaps one of them had "spoken" James's ship.

Mary put away her sewing and rocked the cradle with her foot thoughtfully. "She's smiling, Henrietta. Isn't she a dear! Won't James be surprised to see her!"

"He won't have forgotten she was to be born."

"No-o-! But he's so taken up with whales!"

"Another ship!" Henrietta took up the glass she kept at her side. "Is that the *Merlin?*"

She answered her own question. "No, she rides too high

at the bow. Perhaps—say, Mary, do you recognize that ship?"

Mary took the glass. "Oh, Henrietta, Henrietta! It's the *Seconet!*"

The gathering at the consulate that evening was a joyful one. Mary tried to copy the dignity of the older women who acted as though they had been separated from their husbands for only a week or so. As James sat at the table beside her Mary longed to put her hand in his, but instead she sat very straight beside him listening to his tales. Of all the captains there James could make his stories the most dramatic. He could relive the storms, the death flurry of a whale, the chase with the line burning into the loggerhead as the whaleboat followed a fleeing whale. He could tell of the islands where he had stopped and with a word or two bring out some characteristic that made a vivid picture. He'd tell of ships he'd spoken and damn some captain by a quiet word about his "fat officers and mangy-looking crew."

The other men told stories. One led to another until the whole historic range of whaling was covered by the personal experiences of these men. The evening meal stretched out.

At last Mary was alone with James. He took her in his arms and kissed her gently, "Mary, my little wife," he said. "Did you miss me?" He wanted to add "dear," but he had not been brought up to say such things.

She shook herself free, coyly. "Look!" She pointed towards the sleeping children. "I haven't had time to miss you."

2 4 4

They went softly across the room.

"They're pretty. Look at the little one, sucking her thumb. The older one is a beauty, and she has grown so big and strong. What do you call her, Mary?"

"Niñita."

"I don't like that. When's she going to have a real name?"

"James, I'd like to name them for the women who have been so kind to me here—Alvida Ringgold and Henrietta DeBlois. Would you mind?"

"Mind? No! It's a good idea."

"And—and—could they be christened before we go to sea, in the Catholic church here?"

James had no use for such folderol. But here he was in port. It was a long time since he'd seen Mary. If she'd feel any better for having holy water splashed on the children he guessed they could stand it and so could he.

"All right. We'll have a christening, and by George 'twill be a beauty!"

They made plans that evening, his eagerness finding a ready response. "I'll ask Consul Ringgold to tend to the arrangements and I'll set up a banquet, too, and invite every captain in port."

The hot, dry wind blew outside their window, but Mary didn't mind. She was safe with James beside her. He held her in his arms, and she could smell the sea. She could feel the sea, the throb of it against her, the dip and rise of the waves, the pain and joy of the sea.

The tedium of long days in the Paita heat was over now that James was here with his energy for large affairs.

2 4 5

"How about the christening?" he'd ask his friends, until several of the sea captains postponed their sailings so they could be present.

Dressed in the finest style in their top hats and fine broadcloth in spite of the tropic heat, they were a handsome lot. There were ladies in cool starched gowns, the children in their best, and a long procession of servants and townspeople.

It was not to be wondered at that the little padre was flustered, stumbled from Latin to Spanish, and added an Indian word or two. As the salt was placed on Alvida's tongue, she spat it out, to the secret joy of James and the outward consternation of the priest.

Little Henrietta was more agreeable. She always took what came her way.

For many years Alvida was to hear of her heretical outburst, and she came to be as proud of it as she was ashamed at being compared to the goat.

When they came out of the church, Mary saw James throw a handful of coins into the crowd, and she gasped as she saw that they were gold pieces. One of them rolled to little Alvida's feet, and she picked it up and clutched it in her moist palm. Long afterward Alvida regretted that her mother had induced her to deposit it in the New Bedford Dime Savings Bank to draw interest. As a souvenir of the faroff day in Paita it would have represented much more than a gold dollar on deposit.

The fleet started to thin out in the harbor, and by the end of the month they were again on board the *Seconet* and on their way out into the Pacific.

48

THE equatorial sun blazed down on the *Seconet* as she
rolled slightly in the oily swell. Her smoke-blackened,
weather-worn sails hung limply from the yards and
flapped in the vagrant puffs of wind. The deck planking
sent up shimmering waves of heat.

The cabin was unbearable in its ovenlike closeness, but
here on the poop deck the housing gave shade where
Mary could put the children to sleep. An occasional
down draft from the sail furnished relief.

Up forward some of the men had rigged a sailcloth
as a shelter, and they sprawled under it, limp and inert.
One sailor had baited a hook which he dangled listlessly
over the side.

Captain Cleaveland took his noon reading. "That's
all right," he said. The usual onshore breeze that afternoon and evening would enable them to reach Tumbes
by morning.

Later, little puffs of wind tantalized them by swelling the sails almost enough to give them steerageway and then dying out. Mary went below to rest her eyes from the glare and resigned herself to the heat. The children stretched out on the bed with their fair hair plastered down in wet curls and their white dresses clinging to them.

In the late afternoon a steady breeze sprang up, as James had predicted, and the cool air came in through the ports in puffs that felt like pats of water against their wet bodies. The *Seconet* again became a living thing and moved on toward Tumbes. Sleep came to them at last. When they awoke it was morning.

In the middle of the forenoon the lookout sighted land off the starboard bow, a low fringed shore with breakers showing along a protecting reef. Soon they were in Tumbes Roads, where they dropped anchor. When the ship was once more still and the sails furled, the tropic heat enveloped them again, and the rank smell of vegetation came to them from the nearby land.

The boat crew pulled lazily to the mouth of the river, where the water showed white over the bar. Here all of the men became tense and pulled hard until they were in the calm water of the river. Mary had overcome her first terror of the passage several years ago, but she still shuddered as she saw dozens of ugly snouts as alligators swam their way. Occasionally she saw the dead, whitish gray of a shark's body as he circled the boat, and she felt that the whaleboat was a frail craft to be pulling amongst these killers.

At the consulate Len Sanford greeted them and made them feel at home. Little Alvida remembered Len and

2 4 8

held up her arms to him as she used to do in Paita. He carried her around, showing her little parakeets in cages, and pots of bright jungle flowers.

Darkness in Tumbes shut down like a velvet curtain. In Sydney she had been accustomed to longer twilights, while in West Tisbury there was enough warning so the birds could fuss about with their evening preparations and she could do her chores. The senses adjusted themselves to the gradual change, and when the good darkness set in and the lights twinkled over the brook, she was ready for the night. Here she felt as if she were caught unawares. Darkness came hastily. One moment the slanting rays of sunlight were reflected from the bright green foliage and the gay plumage of the birds, the next— black, impenetrable darkness. Silence reigned at first, as if all nature were shocked, and then the night noises commenced. There were rhythmical throbbing sounds, croaks of tree frogs, rustling in the vegetation, and ominous splashing in the river. Mist streamed up from the hot moist earth and spread out like a lake over the river bed.

That evening as they sat in the consul's study, Len asked Captain Cleaveland whether he knew Captain Fisher.

"Of the *Lancer?* Yes, I know him," James answered warily. "Good whaler."

"Would you want to sail under him," Mary spoke up, "as mate, say?"

"No, be hanged if I would!"

"Len was one of his sailors."

"You don't say so!"

"I jumped ship. I couldn't stand his treatment. He

249

wanted me to go so he could save my pay. Yes, he came into the office about a month ago, and I can tell you he was surprised to see me. He changed color but decided to avoid recognizing me. He wanted to put a sick sailor ashore and get my signature for his discharge."

"Did you give it him?"

"Yes, but first he decided to pay the man his wages and three months' extra pay."

James laughed heartily. Captains like Fisher gave whalers a bad name. He was glad Fisher had met his come-uppance.

After his business in Tumbes was finished, James settled down to enjoy a few days' visit while his men loaded supplies for the next cruise. He bought a gay shawl and a pair of silk stockings for Mary and some little gold ornaments for the children. Gold was plentiful in this tropical town, and everyone appeared to be well off. The women were vain, and many of them wore as many as three or four complete changes of clothes in a day. Mary noticed a shocking lack of taste. Sanford told her that there were five women to every man. James said that accounted for all the gay clothes. "Dressed to kill," he called it.

A regular event in any of their visits to Tumbes was a trip to the oyster trees. They set forth in the boat with bags and baskets and rowed downstream to another branch of the Tumbes River. Here they found trees resembling weeping willows with their branches trailing into the river. These were thickly incrusted with oysters, which were now exposed by the receding tide. They gathered their baskets and bags full and piled heaps in the bottom of the boat until they had a load. James opened one with his clasp knife and tried it.

"They don't come up to Vineyard oysters, but we'll take in a few to help change the diet."

After several days of Sanford's hospitality, James said that the *Seconet* was ready to sail, well stocked with wood and water. He had added to his cargo a supply of the hard algarroba wood to make an armchair. He wanted a good stout desk chair, and he thought the carpenter was smart enough to do the trick with bolts and screws, even if you couldn't get a nail into it.

As they set out the next morning, Len came to the boat to wish them a safe trip home. He wanted to go to his home in upstate New York, as his father was urging him to do, but he wished to stay a few years longer to make a stake and show them that he surely could make good out in the world.

They watched his stocky figure on the shore until the boat reached the turn in the river. Then he raised his panama, waved it, and was lost to sight behind the drooping foliage.

They heard later that he became wealthy by honest, clever trading, and left for a well-earned vacation, eager to present himself, a success, to his father. At Panama he contracted a fever and never reached home.

Mary hugged her babies to her as they shot the bar where the sharks waited and came into the roads. She sighed with relief when she was once more in the snug cabin aboard the *Seconet*. It was good to be safe between the stout bulwarks of James's ship.

49

For a few months they cruised the On Shore Whaling Grounds. Luck was with them, for they took four more whales.

The little girls grew bigger and were interested in everything. Whenever they heard the cry, "Blo-o-ows!" they rushed to see the sport. Mary had to keep close to them lest they get under foot. Alvida watched every move her father made; she noticed each intonation; then when the sailors asked her how she caught whales, she'd stand squarely on the deck, and call, first as captain, then as mate, but getting each command clear and precise. "Mr. Look, stand by to heave her to. Stand by your heads'ls, sheets, and braces. Hard down your wheel." Then, with a final dramatic flourish, "Lower away!"

Once when the whale was made fast to the ship and the cutting stages were in place, one of the men lifted her over the side and let her stand on the whale's back.

As long as she lived she would never forget the sensation, for the whale seemed almost as big as the ship, her world. James wouldn't permit that again.

Mary suggested that they could bathe the children in the warm rains, so James ordered the men to set up a line tub on deck whenever there was a shower. The children splashed and played there while the sailors watched them.

"Just as if they was puppies."

Alvida retained vivid recollections of a few of the events on the remainder of the voyage. She recalled how terror-stricken she was when the men, in sport, got "Mitter Wap-Wap" down on the deck and pretended they were going to cut off his head. She saw the gleaming knife threatening her idol, and her duty was clear. With a shrill scream she rushed into the midst of the sailors with her tiny fists. Her father had to tell the men never again to play a trick like that on Mr. Washburn. She remembered standing on deck and seeing her little pewter flatiron flashing over the side. She loved the little iron. Many nights Mary had taken it from the crib after Alvida had fallen asleep cuddling the hard, unyielding toy. She liked to suck it. Her father had told her often to take it out of her mouth. It felt so good there, and the soft metal chewed off in little shavings, leaving the marks of her sharp, white teeth. One day he warned her, "If you put that flatiron in your mouth again, I'll heave it overboard." He had hardly delivered his ultimatum before she had it in between her teeth, and then she saw it curving over the side in the bright sun and splashing into the Pacific Ocean.

The little girls saw the world around them in flashes: bright sunshine, warm rains, vivid color from sea and sky, white sails, dull smoke with the stench of frying fat; movement, excitement as the boats were lowered; islands in the distance with palm tress waving; ships like their own; ports, noisy, lively; a creaking of timbers, a lapping of waves, wind through the rigging; men—kind, pleasant, carefree, with hard muscles and sun-browned faces; a commanding, all-powerful father, king of their world; a sweet, gentle mother singing lullabies with a voice now sad, now gay.

50

MARY was glad to be going home. They had been in port here in Talcahuano for about two weeks, and tomorrow, March 31, 1860, they were to sail. It was nearly five years now since she had seen the Vineyard. All of her dreams of a home might soon be realized because the ship was full of oil, and according to the latest price quotations James would receive a good sum for his lay.

She had gone back to the scenes of her former visits in Talcahuano. The heights to the west of the town were lovely in their luxurious foliage, and the peak of Sentinele stood out in the rising sun before the rest of the world was bright. This town was not nearly so disagreeable a place as she had once thought, and she had some moments of regret when she thought that she would never see it again.

The *Seconet* weighed anchor later in the morning and sailed out on the tide. Beautiful weather and a fair wind sent the ship along with her courses set, bound around the Horn for home.

Mary worked on shoregoing togs for the children. She was getting more adept with her needle, and the absence of household cares gave her time enough to accomplish a great deal, especially as the sailors often asked to take care of the babies. As she had no patterns, she cut simple little dresses to look like those she recalled seeing before she left New Bedford. They were pretty, made of bright cloth from Talcahuano.

The trip around the Horn this time was uneventful. Cold gray sky, leaden waves, and a hazy line for the shore were all that they could see for several days. Favoring winds sent the vessel around the Cape, and soon she was headed north in the Atlantic. Thousands of miles to go, and much that might happen, yet Mary felt that she was already on the last lap for home.

All the way north they never sighted land. They spoke several ships but did not stop to gam because Captain Cleaveland was eager to make New Bedford before anything happened to the oil market. There had been rumors of unrest between the Northern and Southern states and also talk of a new oil for lamps. This was disquieting, and he would take no chances.

The men were kept busy overhauling the gear and getting things in shape so the ship would present a good appearance when making port. They scrubbed the woodwork with ashes from the galley stove until there was hardly a vestige of oil. Men were aloft much of the time, slushing and scraping down. Not only would the *Seconet* look well entering the harbor, but she would be able to refit sooner and be at sea again for another pay load.

On July 20, at latitude 29 N., longitude 67 W., they spoke the bark *Saxon* bound from Halifax to Havana.

"Pretty close to home when we cut the wake of one of these vessels."

Early in the morning of July 21 all hands were on deck to watch for the eclipse of the sun. The almanac predicted it, but they wanted to see if it actually would happen. One of the sailors said it meant no good. There'd be a war, very likely. At ten minutes after seven they could see a slight dip in the side of the sun. Mary could see it through a little piece of tourmaline that the captain used to detect reefs and breakers in the tropics. In an hour much of the sun was covered, and a chill had descended upon the ocean. Even the wind was subdued, and the men's faces, in the unnatural twilight, looked ghastly. Mary involuntarily crossed herself.

They picked up the pilot at dusk, off Montauk Point, on July 28. Since the night was clear and there would be a moon about midnight, he decided to take them in and make New Bedford in the early morning. There would be high tide at about 4 A.M., so they could make their anchorage before it turned.

Mary tucked the babies in bed and then turned to her packing. There was so pitifully little. Much that she had brought was worn threadbare, and she hadn't bought much in foreign ports. Her best traveling dress was in good condition, and she thought as she laid it aside that she would look well in it and be a credit to James. Then she, too, went to bed, but not to sleep. Every sound of the vessel seemed new and strange. She was aware of the rudder chains as they moved slightly at the helmsman's touch. The ripple of the ocean alongside seemed noisier, and the masts creaked alarmingly. She finally dropped off to a troubled sleep, and when she awoke all was still. She rushed to the port hole, and there all about her were twinkling lights. They were in New Bedford harbor.

When the little girls were dressed, it was fun to show them the sights and tell them they were near home. They were American children, born under the Stars and Stripes, but they had never yet set foot on the shores of the United States. They watched in astonishment the dwellings and warehouses, ropewalks and chandleries. They had never seen a harbor with so many ships and with steam packets and tugs.

When the boat took them ashore and they walked across the cobbled street to the hack, Alvida and Etta missed the swing of the ship beneath them. They staggered, and the elder remarked solemnly to her baby sister, "Heavy sea today!"

They would have to wait until the next day for the customhouse to open. All the lower part of the town was quiet in the summer heat, for there were few people abroad so early Sunday morning. They heard church bells. They began to meet people on their way to church. Mary gasped in astonishment at their outlandish dress. They billowed all about. Two ladies filled the sidewalk, and gentlemen stepped into the gutter to let them pass. As the day wore on she came to the realization that her dress was the one that looked queer. Fashion had moved on in the five years she had been out of the world, and

258

her fine dress was something to be stared at, now that hoop skirts were in style.

The next morning James went early to the custom-house and to his agents. "The price has gone up fifteen cents on the gallon," they told him. He found that the amount of oil he had taken was already well known about town.

"Could I get one of those new hoop skirts, then?" Mary asked.

"Why, yes," James answered, "and bonnets and capes and all the fixings. Only get 'em today. We want to set sail for the Vineyard early tomorrow."

BOOK V

At Home

JULY, 1860
APRIL, 1862

51

IN EARLY July wild roses bloom on Martha's Vineyard, and grapevines tangle in the underbrush, scenting the air with their blossoms. The oak leaves have shed their immature down and gleam with polished brilliance in the sun and wind, making dappled light and shadow on the roadway. Grass is high in the meadows, with redtop waving airily and heavy heads of clover swaying. Meadow larks sing, and orioles—and quail signal, "Bob-white, Bob-bob-white." Over all is the friendly lullaby of the sea lapping the South Shore and the tang of salt.

It seemed like Paradise to Mary after the long months on shipboard in storms with the following swell that made her sick, after the heat that brought out the fatty smell of the oil casks stowed below. All was peaceful here after the creaking and straining of the rigging and the shifting of cargo in the hold. It seemed moderate after the harsh, bright sun of Paita and the strangeness of Talcahuano. Still she dreaded the approach to Mrs. Henry Cleaveland's.

"Can't we go right to our own home, James?" she had asked.

"No, Sylvanus is living there. We'll go to Father's. When Sylvene moves I want to fit up the place so it'll be real modern. We'll have a first-rate house there by the time I'm through."

"Well, it won't be for long," she thought.

Contrary to Mary's expectations, Mrs. Cleaveland greeted her with fine courtesy and even warmth. But Mary's heart ached for the old captain when he came eagerly forward, stumping along with a wooden leg and a cane. He had been such a virile man, always gentle and kind, but emanating a quiet power. There were more lines in his face, deeper furrows even than the weathered lines a sailor gets from watching the sea for whales. These were marks of pain and worry.

Mary Ann and old Captain Cleaveland—yes, old now at sixty—invited them in, and right away the little girls won a place of their own. Alvida curtsied daintily as Mary had taught her to do, then swaggered around with the queer rolling gait she had learned on the pitching vessel.

"Grandmother has a large deck," she said confidentially to Mary.

Mrs. Cleaveland looked them over critically. These were handsome children, but she found a flaw. "How did you get that scar on your forehead, child?" she inquired.

Mary turned white at the memory those words evoked,

but Alvida answered with childish simplicity, "I fell down the main hatchway."

Mrs. Cleaveland looked accusingly at Mary.

"Tell your grandmother," put in James, "how to box the compass, Alvida."

"Where did you ever get that heathen name for her, James?"

They told her about the Catholic christening, and Mrs. Cleaveland's mouth curled. James watched her with a twinkle in his eyes. "She spit out whatever it was they put on her tongue, Ma," he said.

Catholics! She might have known! James hadn't married her in a Catholic church, but she'd got around him somehow. First thing they knew she'd have *him* in a Catholic church, bowing and scraping and crossing himself like the rest of them and saying his prayers in Latin on a string of beads.

"Well, he's made his bed. Let him lie in it!" she thought. But she couldn't let him alone. Her maternal hand would ever be trying to smooth out wrinkles for James.

Then a practical thought gave her sudden comfort. "There's no Catholic church on the Island, no priest. She'd have a hard time bringing them up Catholic. If they mean to fit out Squire George Athearn's place and live in it, I guess they'll have to accept Squire George's religion—or become Baptists." *That* she knew James wouldn't do.

After dinner the men and women gathered around the dining-room table. It seemed as though they couldn't get enough of talking and listening to the events of the last five years. They were brilliant conversationalists, these Cleavelands and Athearns and Looks, and needed only each other for audience, although there were often more, for they attracted other villagers from far and near. Mrs. Cleaveland's comments were interesting and witty—when directed against other people. Today, however, the neighbors passed by discreetly, to give the captain a little time with his family.

Old Captain Cleaveland questioned his son wistfully about doings in the Pacific, about whaling on the Off Shore Grounds, about the new bomb lances. "What's whaling coming to, with all these contraptions!"

In return the home folks told of the doings here—news of their own family. Sylvanus had been sailing the *Mary Wilder* for Almy. He made a good voyage; then Captain Luce took her.

"Yes, we saw Captain Luce in Paita."

"You don't say! Any oil?"

"No, he was clean, then."

"See anything of the *Eliza Adams?* Sylvene was made master of her."

Mrs. Cleaveland was not pleased with Abbie, Sylvanus's wife. She had lived in Holmes's Hole, but she came originally from the Cape. According to Cleaveland standards she was a poor housekeeper. "I don't believe Sylvene has enough to eat half the time," she said, "except when he comes over here for pie and doughnuts and hot bread. They have two real nice children, especially the boy." Mrs. Cleaveland was partial to boys, and besides she wanted Mary to know that even Abbie had one!

Daniel was doing splendidly with his profession. He

seemed to be as pleased with himself as though he was a whaler. He'd built up a nice practice in Holmes's Hole. He'd been elected to the school committee and the health committee. It was getting to be quite the fashion to have him for doctor, though many stuck to Doctor Luce, "from habit," Mrs. Cleaveland thought. "Yes, Dan'l will make out, even if he didn't stay at sea."

"Eliza has two boys now, but Addie's getting set to be an old maid, now she's twenty."

Addie smiled, for Captain Adams had looked inquiringly at her the last time he came up "to see Father."

"Peter Pease and Lottie were married. And say! You ought to see Saphrony Cathcart! She married a good-for-nothing critter, and he went off and left her."

"Say, that's hard lines."

"You'd be surprised at how it woke her up. She doesn't go around moping. She's started a millinery business in the Cathcart house, and when things are dull she goes out to dressmaking. She goes clear to Boston to study the styles."

"She always had considerable spunk."

"Well, kind of a passive spunk. She never had any real vim till William Lawton stirred her up."

"Where'd he come from?"

"Land knows. Somewhere from off."

"Where'd he go?"

"To the South Seas, they tell me. Nobody knows whether he intends to come back or not."

Now they heard the details of Father's accident. He had been to Holmes's Hole to see about some supplies and gear he was to take with him on his next voyage, for he was to leave soon. On the way back old Hunter had been too eager to get to the barn, had rounded the corner on one wheel, thrown Father out, and dragged him the rest of the way home. His leg was badly broken above the knee. Right away they had sent for Doctor Luce, but he could do nothing to save it. So he took a carpenter's saw, Henry gritted his teeth, and without more ado Dr. Luce amputated the leg.

"They've got something now to put you to sleep while they're cutting you," James said.

"Anybody that could sleep through that must be pretty hardy," said Father.

It took him a long time to recover; then he realized that he would never be fit to go to sea again. At last he bought a wooden leg and looked about for something to occupy his mind. It was then that Thomas Bradley offered for sale the factory at the mill brook. Six hands were kept busy there the whole time, with extra ones just after shearing. They made a fine smooth cloth for men's suits. "The cloth is so firm that once a suit's made it'll last a lifetime."

"That's not very good for your business, Pa."

Father ignored that remark. "I don't know, though, how long I can stand out against these great mills at Lawrence and Lowell."

"No doubt Bradley saw the handwriting on the wall when he sold," James thought.

"Some of the stores even buy goods from off island," the old captain complained, "though it stands to reason they can't make material in such quantities and have it good."

The Squire George Athearn *house* after Captain James Cleaveland *had it remodeled*

"What is the great building opposite the blacksmith shop?"

"That is the Agricultural Hall. They are to have a fair there each year with exhibits of all sorts, and prizes."

"Your father is a trustee," Mrs. Cleaveland announced proudly. "He was on the first committee of arrangements. There were nearly two thousand people there the first year, and I guess more the second."

Their talk turned farther afield to national issues. They discussed the Abolitionists—"The crazy fools are going too far"—the Fugitive Slave Law, the Dred-Scott decision, the Lincoln-Douglas debates, Abraham Lincoln's rise on the political horizon, and what would be the result of the next presidential election. The Cleavelands liked that man Lincoln—keen and witty and like folks.

It took many evenings to exhaust the news of events of the last five years. Mrs. Cleaveland was quite tolerant of Mary. In the daytime Mary and the little girls, and sometimes Mrs. Cleaveland too, drove around with James, delivering personal messages from seamen still in the Pacific and consulting with the neighbors about his house.

He hired Moses Vincent to remodel his place after a sea captain's idea of architecture. He tore out the wooden paneling of Squire George Athearn's time. He made the windows high and large and plastered all around them. He tore off the roof to reshingle, to make a broad sheltering overhang, and to add a lookout.

"Fine," said the captain. "Now, I hope nobody dies before you get that roof sealed up," for Moses Vincent was undertaker as well as carpenter.

2 6 9

Mary went over regularly with the children. She loved the smell of new cedar shingles and the sound of the hammers with their sharp firm taps as they hit each nail. It was their own house. It was their own ground, stationary underfoot. It was their own orchard with pears ripening and early Maiden's Blush apples.

She spent long days in the sun with the children running around. "Oh, pretty flowers growing on deck," Etta would say, grasping great handfuls of grass or weeds. Alvida would watch everything in silence or suddenly run to examine something at a little distance and fall over, for the level ground still seemed unnatural.

They still swung from side to side awaiting the roll of the deck that no longer lurched beneath them. "It's very rugged, today," they'd say.

Soon they came to accept the Island as their home and to love it as they had loved the ship.

52

To MARY it seemed a long time before their home was ready. A month later they were still living with James's parents, and Mary and her mother-in-law were beginning to get on edge. Little things affected them. A chance remark would be taken seriously, and words that were not entirely innocent bit deep.

Today everything seemed serene. This picnic would be fun.

James was waiting by the horse's head. "I'm not quite sure this critter'll stand. He's apt to head out through the gate any minute." He didn't blame the horse for wanting to get started. A nice day like this everybody was eager to set sail. James wanted to, himself, but Ma hadn't come out of the house yet. The little girls, all dressed, were picking mayweed. Mary was still stowing baskets under the seat.

James liked to watch her. She was so tiny—like a little

girl. Her curls shook as she worked, and her eyes were dark, shaded by their long thick lashes.

"Lucky Lem Tilton was sick, eh, Mary?"

"Why, James!"

"You know what I mean. You're glad you're going, eh?"

"To be sure I am."

Mary had a cute way, James thought, of wriggling with pleasure. "If Lem had kept his health, they'd have had the clambake on the Fourth of July, as they always do."

"Oh!"

"And we'd have been on the Atlantic Ocean, 36 degrees north latitude. That's where the *Seconet* was then. Got your bathing suit, Mary?"

"Yes."

"Have you got *mine?*" James said this eagerly. He loved the sea. He always wanted to go in bathing when he was at home.

Mary wondered why, during the years at sea, he had never gone in swimming. Perhaps it was not in keeping with the dignity of a captain while in command of a ship. She felt in the basket to make sure she had included his warm long-legged swimming suit that he had bought in New Bedford the day after they landed. "It's right here, wrapped up in a towel."

"What's hindering us, now?" James asked impatiently. Then in his quarter-deck voice he shouted, "All a-bo-ar-d!" And when Mrs. Cleaveland appeared, flushed with haste or anger, he said "What's got you anchored, Ma?"

272

"I've had to go around picking up after those three children of yours."

"Three?" James asked idly, but Mary knew she had been included in that category.

Mary had already put the baby in front and had climbed in beside her. Now James helped his mother into the back, then lifted Alvida high over his head and let her down gradually into the back seat.

"Heigh-ho, blow the man down," he shouted to her in the rhythm of a sea chantey.

"Stand by to man the weather braces," Alvida called irrelevantly. James loved to hear his daughter's ship commands. At four years of age she could appreciate the intricacies of sailing as Mary would never be able to. Even Ma wasn't with him as completely as this little girl.

He climbed in beside Mary, took up the reins, and they started off at a brisk trot. Mary slipped a jacket on little Henrietta and tied the bonnet under her chin while James was talking.

"As nice a day as I've seen for the clambake. A good breeze for the boat races. Those young fellows think they are pretty smart if they can maneuver a catboat around a buoy in Tisbury Great Pond. Likely they're making believe it's a whale they're after. *We* used to."

Mrs. Cleaveland answered, but Mary wasn't listening. She readjusted the baby's bonnet absently. She felt the vibration of the carriage like a ship at sea. And James was talking whales again!

The air brushed by, blowing wispy curls against Mary's face and neck, stinging her lips. It brought the color back to her cheeks. She looked down at the baby, contentedly sucking her thumb and twisting a fold of her dress around her finger.

Sand crunched under the wheels, but their horse was strong. He didn't stop for a little sand. James had bought him the day after they arrived, when he found oil had gone up fifteen cents a gallon and he had plenty of money for spending. The carriage was firm and sturdy. James had ordered it especially made. Their clothes were cool and comfortable. With his visored cap and his loose-woven suit James looked distinguished. She herself was wearing a pretty bright calico that she had made. She hummed a little song.

They passed a truck wagon, drawn by a scrawny horse. Hiram Luce had piled his family into it and the long legs of the oldest boys were dangling down in back. "Shiftless critter," James commented, and his mother told him a story or two to back up this opinion.

They overtook a buggy, and looking back James saw Richard Thompson and Eliza M. "By George, I believe they're hitched, now. When we went to sea he was still courting her."

"Yes, they got married shortly after you left."

"Now there's a good handsbreadth between them on the seat."

"Who's that ahead?"

"It's Captain Flanders. Come on, we'll race him."

"But he has a lighter wagon, James," Mary said.

"James has got a better horse," said his mother with a superior air.

"Ship ahoy!" James called.

Captain Flanders didn't look around. He recognized

2 7 4

the voice, even though the last time he had heard it was when they were gamming aboard ship in the Pacific. He knew Captain Cleaveland had a new horse, but so, by Godfrey, had he. He'd come in on the same high tide of oil. He moved to one side of the road, and as Captain Cleaveland came alongside he slapped the horse's flank with the reins, shouting, "Git ap, there!" The horse was startled. He leaped into the air and then let out in long strides.

Now Mary's sporting blood was up. "Go on, James. Don't let him get ahead. Go on. He isn't going fast. He's just going up and down."

"Can't beat a fool that drives the way he does."

"You didn't even try!"

"Now don't go telling me what I didn't do. You can't go tearing over the roads with a wife and children along."

"Perhaps we should have stayed at home."

"Maybe so."

Mary said no more. They drove along quietly, passing other vehicles and making polite bows. Mrs. Cleaveland was chuckling amiably in back, talking sweetly to little Alvida. They could see the dust from Captain Flanders' wagon curling out ahead of them.

The spontaneous fun of the day had gone for Mary.

They entered the woods at Nab's corner. There would be no more passing here, for the trees were thick, arching overhead, and the road was like a thin green tunnel.

The cool quietness of the place seemed to fall on Mary's spirit peacefully. She wanted to say, "I'm sorry." But sorry for what? The remark James had taken so seriously hadn't been important.

She tried to talk on another subject, "Hark, is that a woodpecker?"

"No, a flicker."

She didn't like his patronizing tone. A flicker was certainly a woodpecker. Hadn't one pecked out a huge hole in their apple tree for a nest?

"What's the matter with you today, Mary?" James asked.

Mary didn't answer. At sea James was as big as the ocean. Since he'd been at home he had become trivial, irritated at unimportant matters, at least when his mother was around. "We might be so happy," she thought. "Perhaps in our own home things will be different. If only we can get there soon enough!"

As they drove along the woods became thinner and grayer. The southwest wind had bent the trees and stunted them, but as a summer breeze it came to their nostrils with a delightful fragrance. The feel of it was exhilarating, and it brought the surf noise to them.

James handed the reins over and got out to open the gate. "Drive along through, Mary."

"Couldn't you leave it open for the Tilton family? They are close behind," Mary called to him.

"And have West Mitchell's sheep go straying through the woods!"

"A fine way to repay him for letting us use his land!" Mrs. Cleaveland commented.

Mary felt like crying. She couldn't say anything without its being misunderstood and twisted into something unpleasant.

53

BEYOND the gate they came out into a stretch of open pasture. From there they could see people at the grove. There were teams and buggies full, children running and shrieking at their games, men piling driftwood on the fire, women setting the tables. As they approached they recognized people from Chilmark, from Holmes's Hole, and from their own town.

The underbrush had been cleared away from the dwarf oak grove near the ocean, except for the fringe of hazel bushes which gave protection from the southwest wind. At the eastward there was a pile of rocks and quantities of driftwood that had been gathered in wagonloads and brought to this spot the day before. Lem Tilton, master of the bake, had started a roaring fire on the rocks, and when they were thoroughly heated he would scrape away the coals, pile on rockweed, put in the food—all the good sea things and vegetables from Island farms, separating each layer of food with a layer of wet seaweed. Then he would cover the whole mound with a large piece of sailcloth and let things steam.

It would be an hour before Lem would be ready. They wandered over to the shore of the pond. James and Alvida went ahead. Mary walked slowly, keeping pace with little Henrietta.

From the point they could see all over Tisbury Great Pond—up Town Cove with the church spire, the Agricultural Hall, the stores and houses of the village nestling among the trees. They could see the head of Tiah's Cove where there was another cluster of buildings. Deep Bottom was farther away, but smoke from the few remaining Indian wigwams could be seen rising above the pine trees. Middle Cove was lost behind the bars that seemed to have formed across its mouth. Clear across the Great Pond the sturdy farmhouse of the Johnsons could be seen at Long Point.

They watched the boat races, James cheering vociferously for the Look boys, who won. James was always the center of any group. Even when they came back to the grove and sat down at the table, two or three other captains and their wives asked to join him at the same long table.

Mary sat quite still, absorbed in turning first to Henrietta and then to Alvida with a spoonful of clam broth. Mrs. Cleaveland didn't offer to help. She was busy talking.

"Hello," Mrs. Cleaveland said, "Here's Saphrony Cathcart!" She didn't bother with Sapronia's married name. She'd never approved of Saphronia's husband.

Saphronia stepped along, smart in her Boston clothes —a full stiff skirt and neat little jacket. A wide straw hat trimmed with poppies bent jauntily over her forehead and over her hair in back.

"James!" She stretched her hand across the table to him.

"Why, 'Phrony!" James rose, clasped her outstretched hand, and stared at her, frankly admiring her looks. "Godfrey," he exclaimed, "I haven't seen you for—what is it—ten, twelve years. You've changed!"

"You make me feel old and decrepit," she said, laughing.

"You don't look *old*," James answered earnestly, "but you look different."

Mary looked up to smile, but Saphronia didn't look her way at all, not even to notice the children, who were pretty and clean in their neat cotton dresses. But she bent down to kiss James's mother.

"Sit down here, 'Phrony." Then, looking over her shoulder, "Move over, Mary."

"Certainly." Mary squeezed the two children closer on the bench. Mrs. Cleaveland moved along, too, and seated Saphronia on the other side, almost turning her back towards her daughter-in-law. James was sitting opposite them.

The food kept coming to the tables—clams steamed in seaweed, lobsters, sweet potatoes, corn, chicken. Mary was kept busy supplying three plates with the proper food, helping the children select what was good for them, and cutting up pieces of chicken. She listened absent-mindedly to the conversation. It was mostly about people she had never known. Occasionally some familiar ship or captain was mentioned, and she looked up to say with her eyes, "Is that the one we met in Talcahuano or Paita?" She and James had always been able to talk to each other like that in a crowd. But James was preoccupied today. He wasn't looking for her signals, waiting to give a response.

James couldn't help looking at Saphrony. Why, she must be thirty-nine or forty. She was a year or two older than he was. Wasn't that strange now! Some of the pretty girls he used to court had grown fat and blowsy, but 'Phrony! Like enough he'd have married 'Phrony before he went to sea if she hadn't been so homely. Well, things had turned out all right as they were!

After the pies and watermelon all the women helped gather things together. "Sit still, Mary," they said, "you have the children to look after."

Mary would have liked to help. Mrs. Cleaveland might have looked after the children for a few minutes and let her be with the other young women, but she didn't offer.

The men were drawing on their pipes, raising great clouds of smoke. They were telling stories and grinning self-consciously over those that were not fit for the women to hear. James didn't even smile when the others looked that way. He puffed solemnly on his pipe, but he was not quiet for long. He was launched on a story of ships or storms or stove-in whaleboats, and the others were clustered about him, listening. But James's eyes followed Saphronia as she stacked the plates on the tables.

Mary sat in the shade of a tree, rocking the baby in her arms, singing softly, "Rockaby, baby, on the treetop."

The little girl was sleepy. The gentle motion was like the soothing swing of the ship. She was soon fast asleep and didn't waken when Mary laid her gently on a blanket.

Alvida was showing some other children how to climb the ratlines, using a tree to illustrate. "It's fortunate there are no tall trees here," Mary thought.

With the children taken care of, Mary went to help the women, but they were through with their work.

"Come on, girls," they said. "We'll go swimming. Our dinner will be digested by the time we get to the beach and get into our bathing suits. Did you bring yours, 'Phrony?"

"Yes, she has a new one."

Mary was afraid she wouldn't be able to go. Henrietta was still asleep, but Mrs. Cottle came to her, "I'll look out for your little ones, Mary."

So she went as part of a jolly group down towards the old barns where the beach ploughs were kept. The young women dressed in the stalls there, while the men went into Torrey's net house to change.

The first woman ready and the first to plunge into the water was Mary. She had learned to swim with her brothers in Sydney and she swam beautifully. "Come on in, James. It's fine."

James, usually eager for the water, was standing on the shore talking to Saphronia Cathcart, until finally she mustered her courage and struck out from the shore. Now James could have his swim. He went way out with the other men.

By this time most of the girls had been in the water long enough. Fifteen minutes was the prescribed time for a bath, and then one must exercise vigorously until dry.

A shriek! All turned to see Saphronia struggling in the water.

They called to the men, each woman to a different one, "James!" "Frank!" "Josiah!" "Look out for 'Phrony!"

James was a splendid swimmer, and he was nearest. He reached her first, held her up, dragged her to the shore. She lay limp in his arms.

The girls gathered around. Eliza had a bottle of smelling salts. Martha chafed her wrists. Betsy threw a warm shawl about her.

"Strange I didn't notice any hole there where she was swimming."

"Nor I."

Mary hadn't either.

The girls hovered over her, helping her dress, while James got ready quickly. "I'll take her back to the grove," he said.

Other men were ready to help, but James carried her easily. She was light—taller than Mary but very slender. They all trooped back to the picnic grounds, solemnly.

Some of the younger boys ran ahead to tell the women that Saphrony Cathcart had almost got drowned.

"You don't suppose," one of the older women whispered to another, "you don't suppose life was too hard for her?"

"Oh, no, no!" But the other spoke without conviction.

Mrs. Cleaveland did little speculating. She was all for action.

"One of you men have our team ready by the time the

282

captain gets here," she commanded. "Take one of the stones, still warm from the bake, wrap it up, and put it on the floor of the carriage." And when James arrived, "Take her home, James, as quick as you can, and tell old Mis' Cathcart to put her to bed."

"Perhaps Captain Flanders . . . " Mary started to say, thinking of his fast horse and lighter wagon and the fact that he had no family to come back for. But she bit her lip before she said it. They would think she was afraid to have Saphronia Cathcart ride with her husband.

54

AFTER that day at the beach Mary saw a great deal of Saphronia. She came to Mrs. Cleaveland's nearly every morning with a pie made of especially prepared fruit that she wanted Mrs. Cleaveland to try or with questions about dressmaking and styles.

It was quite a long walk back home, so Mrs. Cleaveland often said, "Hitch up the team, James, and take 'Phrony back." He wasn't very busy just now, and he had to go to the store anyway.

Mary began to realize that Saphronia Cathcart went driving with James nearly as often as she herself did. Mary was always busy with the children each morning when James took Saphronia home.

"Well," thought Mary, "she isn't very attractive. She's tall and thin, and her speech is colloquial in spite of her studied airs. And she is older—why, she's ten or twelve years older than I. She's older than

James by a year or two. If we could only get into our own home!"

As soon as the children were bathed and dressed she took them across the fields to the house. Each time it looked more and more imposing. A big place it was—two stories and a half—the largest in the village. It was as fine looking as any of the great Edgartown houses built by the wealthiest sea captains. Mary would have preferred a smaller one—one that she could manage herself. But she would have Sarah Ann, Caroline's sister, to help her, and that would be well. She wouldn't be tied down as much as she had been at her mother-in-law's, for Mary Ann Cleaveland never offered to help her with the children. Sarah Ann was capable with children and a "faculized" cook. All she lacked was brains for managing, and Mary could supply those.

Mary could have parties here—quilting bees, sewing circles, and chowder suppers for the church. (She realized immediately that she would have to worship in the Congregational Church, so she accepted it.) She'd have all the affairs that the villagers attended—and more. She was to have a piano. She'd have musicales, too.

"If only we could get in soon!"

So she went to Tim and with a few little twists to her words got him to hurry with the doorframes so Painter West could get to work. "It's here I want to be, to be sure, not imposing on my mither-in-law."

"I understhand, to be sure," he said and turned his back to screw one eye into a wink—all to himself.

And to Moses Vincent she made a direct appeal. "We shouldn't be living with James's folks any longer. We'll come over here as soon as you can possibly get the roof tight over our heads. You can finish at your leisure."

"Sensible little woman, young Mrs. Cleaveland," he told his wife later.

James had never seen work done so fast. "I tell y'u," he said, "come around with money in your pocket, and ideas in your head—tell 'em what you want, and you'll get it done. Just look at my house, now." It was gleaming with white paint set off with green shutters.

Inside, Painter West was decorating the fireplaces to look like marble, white with black streaks in the front rooms and dark, like Italian marble, in the other rooms. The doors were hung, and he was graining those in the dining room to look like natural wood. Those in the parlor were smooth white with blue panels. Mary would have little blue flowers in the wallpaper. She sang while the men worked, picturing as she did so a plan for placing the new rosewood piano James had ordered from Boston. The sofa with the carved back could go along that wall, and above it one of the pictures that had been in their cabin on the *Seconet*. The other one—the beautiful girl in the shawl—could go between the windows. The large mahogany table Mrs. Cleaveland had given James could go in the hall, opposite the staircase that had been especially designed and installed by an expert from New Bedford. "Most stairways are too small," James said.

Early in October they left Mrs. Cleaveland's. "How James is twitched about!" was her comment.

"Mary, the plaster is still wet!" James announced.

"It'll dry out better with us living here, keeping up the fires."

2 8 6

"If we don't ketch our death of cold in the meantime."

"But isn't it nice, James, to be in our own home!" She pulled down his head roughly to kiss him.

With her arms reaching up around his shoulders, her face looking eagerly into his, she said, "James, it's beautiful here. You won't ever want to leave it will you, to go to sea again?"

"Why, we've just got back," he answered. He wasn't even thinking of another voyage.

And yet Mary felt she had said the wrong thing. There was something within him that she could not touch.

55

BY SPRING James had grown more and more restless. There would be war as sure as anything. Some of the Southern states were talking of seceding. Lincoln wouldn't stand for that. He had declared that the Constitution made of the states a perpetual union, and the union must be saved.

James spent hours in the big kitchen smoking his pipe and talking with the men who came in to gam. He went over to his mother's to discuss the news in the papers, to hear her clever comments, and to talk with Father. Mary wouldn't go out with James now, and James couldn't go to sea. He'd promised Mary he would stay.

Spring passed, and summer came with its sudden burst of foliage. The mock orange bush under the east window had started blooming when Mary felt the sudden pain that she had grown to recognize as the forerunner of birth.

James sent for Daniel quickly. It was luck to have a

2 8 8

doctor in the family now. James turned over the case to him and went out to the barn. He wished he were at sea. He'd been at sea when the others were born.

Hours later Daniel found him there. "You've a fine big girl, sir," he said professionally.

"The third one," said James. "I wanted a boy."

"Mary . . ." began the doctor, uncertain how to tell him he must be very careful of her.

"God . . ." This was the beginning of a fervent prayer. For the moment he had forgotten what Mary had been through.

"She'll be all right, James, but she's had a hard time."

James went into the house humbly. He washed his hands at the kitchen pump, dried them thoroughly, combed his hair, and put on his tie. "Too bad," he said to himself, "what women have to go through—all on account of Eve and that snake!"

In the east chamber Mary was lying with her eyes shut, and nestled close was the baby, a tiny dark-haired girl. James was just about to say, "Kind of a wizened-up little thing," when Mary awoke.

"I'm sorry, James, she isn't a boy," turning away to hide her tears.

"Don't cry, Mary, don't," he said helplessly. "Look at her!" (He had heard that homely babies made handsome adults.) "She's going to be the prettiest one of all. I want to name her Mary Wilder."

"After a ship!"

"The one I was commanding when we first met!"

And so it was decided.

56

THE big silver poplar at the front gate was shivering in the wind, and as the branches turned up, showing the under side of the leaves, the east room took on a silvery hue. Mary watched the light playing over little Mary Wilder, asleep in one end of the rockall while she sat in the other end sewing. She was humming softly to the baby, but her mind was not on the tune. She was thinking of James.

James had been ill at ease lately. He had been mounting to the lookout for a glimpse of the sea. He'd look to the south, over fields and woods to the Tisbury Great Pond and on to the ocean. Sometimes with his glass he'd pick up an outgoing ship. "I ought to be at sea," he'd say.

With this tense feeling in the air, this bitterness between one set of human beings and another, Mary dreaded having him go. "Wait only a little while, until the war is over," she would say to herself so fervently that she hoped

HENRIETTA DEBLOIS CLEAVELAND
ALVIDA RINGGOLD CLEAVELAND
MARY WILDER CLEAVELAND

her thought would be transmitted. She knew it would be useless to say anything about it to James.

At the store and around the hearths of the village everyone was discussing the war. The first serious battle had been fought, the Battle of Bull Run, a Federal defeat. James was pessimistic. "These Southerners are used to nothing but fighting. They haul out their swords at the drop of a hat—and here they are right on their own territory. We have the sailors and the shipping, if the government only had the sense to make use of them." Fighting on land, to James, was petty business.

There was still plenty to do around the place, but Mary sensed that James was getting bored. A good "cruise" after fruit or nuts would be a diversion. What could they find this time of year? And then she remembered that Betsy had shown her a cluster of wild grapes, but she wouldn't tell where they had grown.

"James, do you know where Betsy could have picked wild grapes?"

James looked up from his accounts with interest. "On the Long Cove Road, likely. They've been growing there ever since I can remember, good years and bad. This is a good year for grapes, they say. Come on! I'll hitch up this afternoon and take you down. Take along plenty of baskets. Want to ask Addie? She's good at picking."

"To be sure."

"I'll go over after dinner and see if she wants to go. You rig yourself up in your oldest clothes and be ready by the time I get back."

Knowing how James felt about waiting, Mary hurried with her preparations. She wore one of her old wool dresses—warm, but no longer fashionable. The bushes wouldn't tear it, and she could slide through among the vines to get at the hanging clusters. She tied a scarf over her head and gathered together the biggest baskets from the buttery and woodhouse. Then she sat by the window where she could watch the gateway. She hummed to herself, beating time on the window sill.

She could see the village stretched peacefully in the autumn afternoon. She could hear the hammer strike the anvil at the blacksmith shop. She could smell wood smoke and piccalilli and quinces.

Ah! Here was James!

"Oh firetown! He's got that woman with him!" To herself—"And she's not dressed for crawling in the underbrush. Addie is, but not she! And James will play the host while Addie and I pick grapes. We'll see!"

"Sarah Ann!" she called. "Get the children ready. Be quick! I'm going to take them. Then you can take the baby and go to see your sister this afternoon if you like."

"Hurry!" she urged herself. "I mustn't keep him waiting. Come on, Alvida, dear. You may go after all, and sit in the front seat with Father."

The little girl jumped up and down in glee. "Come on, sisser," she called to Henrietta. "We're going on a cruise."

They couldn't stop for appropriate clothes, so Mary put pinafores over their dresses. "That'll do very nicely!" she said as James called out, "Ship ahoy, there!" He sounded real pleased with himself. James was always at his best before an audience.

As he got out to come in for the baskets the girls ran to him. "Father, Father, we're going, too. Can I steer?" Alvida hadn't forgotten the thrill of holding the big wheel in the afterdeck of the *Seconet*.

"I'll take the back seat, James," said Mary. "I promised the little girl she could have my seat in front with you." And going out she said, "Good day, Saphrony! I didn't know you were coming. No, no, sit right where you are. Etta and I will sit in back with Addie."

They drove through wood roads that led to the longest cove, the one that cut way back into the plains, through Willow Tree Hollow where the Scotch broom grows, up the hill where the sandy road whirred through the wheel spokes, through the yellowing scrub oaks that were interspersed with masses of brighter goldenrod and banks of purple asters. They skirted the hollow where it was muddy even in dry weather and went past the big trees that stood in a cluster at the edge of a clearing. Mary watched James. She expected him to look back at her and smile, for they had hidden a little whale-ivory man in a hole in the largest oak the first year she had come.

James didn't look around. He was pointing toward the grove with his whip. "There's a tree there with . . . " he was telling Saphrony. He was telling *her!*

"James! Look!" Mary almost screamed in her desire to distract his attention from their secret. She couldn't bear to have Saphrony share it. "There are some grapes, James."

"Pshaw! That's nothing to what you'll see later."

They had passed the oak trees.

"We used to come here every year with Mother,"

Addie said. "And nearer the ocean there are hazelnuts, too. October's the nicest time of all."

"Now, here's the place. I'll hitch the horse to that tree, and we'll meet here with full baskets."

"I'm really not dressed for such an expedition." Saphronia announced. "I'll . . . "

"Why, the children can stay here with you, then," Mary interposed hastily. "I wondered how we should ever keep them from getting scratched."

"You should have left them at home, Mary," James said.

"But they're having such a good time, to be sure."

So Mary lightheartedly filled the largest container, singing softly to herself.

She looked down the still blue water of the cove as far as the ocean. The surf was humming steadily against the shore beyond the Great Pond. Sea gulls settled peacefully on the water, and a tern flashed down into it.

As she looked she saw James wave to her from across the cove and heard his voice raised in raucous song.

Addie was humming softly.

In the carriage Saphronia sat with the children. Henrietta was sleeping in a warm blanket on the floor, but Alvida was standing up shouting sea commands.

"You'll fall, child," 'Phrony kept saying, until after a while she hoped the child would. Saphrony looked more tired than those who came back with full baskets of grapes, torn clothes, and scratched faces.

"Now it's sister's turn for the front seat, Alvida. Would you like to hold her, Saphrony?"

294

"Mercy, no. I shouldn't know how. I'll sit in back."

Sitting beside James with the little girl in her arms, Mary sang lullabies and madrigals all the way home.

"That round went to me," she said to herself as she alighted.

57

MARY was sitting by the window with her sewing in her lap, looking out towards the village. There was Emily Baxter going down the lane. She hadn't been in for a long time. Mary hadn't seen much of her since the *Seconet* had come back from sea. Emily always seemed to be with Saphronia Cathcart. And Sarah Manter and Sarah C, too. She had seen so much of them when she was staying at Caroline's. Well, she hadn't returned their calls. It was her own fault. But she didn't feel like going out as she used to. She didn't feel gay and carefree any more. "I don't seem to be so sociable—since I've had the children," she explained to Caroline and Betsy. But within her heart she knew it wasn't because of the children.

There were times during that winter when she and James had recaptured moments like those of their earliest days together. The newly remodeled old house was a joy that they shared. They both liked company and gaiety, and they could afford to entertain. But it often seemed to Mary as though there was some insidious presence between them. At their own table when they had guests Mary had looked up to catch James's eye and had found that Saphronia Cathcart had taken his attention first. Well, she was sitting nearer. It was natural, and yet they'd always been able to talk that way, quietly between themselves. It was one of the things that had upheld Mary's spirits at Mrs. Cleaveland's.

No matter how much she argued with herself that these exchanges between Saphronia and James were unimportant, somehow Mary began to feel her dislike for the woman growing. She found herself making an apparently innocent thrust at her—one that James, with his man's lack of sensibility, couldn't recognize but that all the women did. They'd look up at Mary quickly, suspiciously, and find her daintily eating her dinner.

"It couldn't have been chance!" they said. "She must feel pretty deep." Some pitied her; some laughed at her. A few admired her quickness of tongue and mind, but Mary hated herself.

Lately Saphronia had given up coming to their home, but she was always to be found at Mrs. Henry Cleaveland's, where she was dressmaking. On Sunday evenings James would tell stories, as he had so often, but now he was telling them, not to the other men, but for feminine approval. Mary knew—and so did Saphronia Cathcart.

Mary began to stay away from those Sunday evenings on one pretext or another, and James began to go over more often on weekdays, too. "Maybe Ma needs this." "Maybe Ma wants to go to Holmes's Hole."

Mary could picture during the frequent trips home a certain growing comradeship between James and Saphronia, carefully encouraged by Mrs. Cleaveland. Not that she wanted an open break! She knew her son well enough to believe that to be impossible. But she wanted to tease Mary, to make her uncomfortable, to see her complacency begin to desert her. She had been so sure of James!

And now when he came home, instead of talking freely as he always had, telling what he'd done and where he'd been, he seemed subdued. She'd ask questions, trying to encourage him to be like himself, but he'd answer in monosyllables in a manner that accused her of prying.

Sometimes men came to the house on an errand, "Is James going to Old Town next week?"

Mary had to confess, "I haven't heard him say."

Sam or John would look incredulous, as much as to say, "Strange wife—don't know her husband's business."

She'd try to smooth things out. "Last time I heard him speak about going was when he was talking to you. Didn't he say definitely, then?"

Sam only grinned a sheepish sort of grin, as much as to say, "Think I'd give the man away?"

More than once she had been humiliated by just such a scene.

Mary got up suddenly, and went to the mirror. At twenty-five she was just as attractive as she used to be—more so, she thought, than when James first met her. Her

2 9 8

hair was as curly and shone from brushing. Her eyes were the same blue-gray, deep-set. Her cheeks and lips were full and healthy. Only around her mouth there was perhaps a little strained look from smiling when she wanted to cry. And her eyes had lost some of their calmness.

No, the fault was not in *her* looks. Saphronia had improved. She had style and dressed well. There was a sprightliness to her manner, a knowledge of the Island things that coincided with James's and gave color to her conversation. She had a look that felt a new-found power and a maturity that Mary lacked.

Mary brushed the curls up quickly from her neck, pulled her hair straight back from her forehead and away from her ears. She looked older, almost thirty. She stood back from the mirror to get the full effect.

"Hey!" The west door opened. It was James.

"Well, well, what you got your hair up that way for? You look like . . . " he paused for an adequate simile, "like the devil!" She pulled out the hairpin and shook her hair free once more.

"Say, I'm going to Holmes's Hole," he announced.

"Oh can I g . . . " she paused. She wouldn't ask to go and be refused, and she saw by his look that he had other plans.

"I won't be home to supper."

She walked over to him. "James . . . " She put her arm around his neck easily as he stood on the lower step in the doorway. But he didn't look up. He stiffened suspiciously. Could she talk to him frankly? Oh, surely she must be able to. She must make him see. She swallowed the lump that kept coming to her throat, making

her want to cry. "James . . . if you should take 'Phrony
—" she hurried. She had to get all the words out before
he stopped her, before she was stopped by the look in his
face. "If she should go with you, don't take her to the
Mansion House, please. She has relatives in Holmes's
Hole she could go to." Mary took her arm away from
him, for his shoulder felt lifeless. She stood back.

"I had no notion of taking her." He looked at her
squarely. "I can't abide jealousy in a woman."

"It's not that, James. I know you love me. But she's
always with you, and it looks—it makes me look—I feel
. . . Oh, James, don't let her spoil everything by making
talk."

"Talk! What's talk of that sort but ideas of filthy-
minded people!"

"But we don't want filthy-minded people talking
about us."

"They'll talk anyway, if they want to. Come on, get out
and forget it. Go to the sewing circle, and then the wom-
en will have to gossip about somebody else. I'll wait for
you to get your things on and take you up there. Ma's
going."

"She'll uphold the family honor," Mary said in an
undertone. Oh, she hoped James hadn't heard her. That
remark was catty. Loudly she added, "No, I'll play and
sing. I can get up to A now easily."

"Go on through the alphabet, then. No telling when
I'll be home. Don't sit up for me." He wouldn't give her
the satisfaction of telling her he was merely going to the
Men's Patriotic Rally. "Godfrey, when I was at sea I
didn't have anybody checking up on me . . . "

"Then it can't be my fault, for I was at sea with you most of the time."

"If there'd been another woman on board there'd have been trouble enough."

"To be sure there would. One at a time is plenty!" What was the use of talking. She would never again mention Saphronia Cathcart's name. But her presence would stay in Mary's mind the more persistently.

58

MRS. CLEAVELAND went to the sewing circle that afternoon, but she didn't enjoy herself as much as usual. From the very start things had gone wrong. She had been waiting for James, and James was a long while coming, so she had hailed Eliza Thompson and driven on with her. Eliza had acted queerly—as though she had something in her mouth and couldn't spit it out.

"Now what's on your mind, Elizy," Mrs. Cleaveland had asked finally, but she hadn't received much satisfaction. That was where Richard Thompson got his queer ways—from his mother! His father was peculiar, too. Kind of half-made, with short legs. "Gets his strange looks from the Thompsons and his strange actions from the other side! Poor Richard!" she thought.

And at the sewing circle they'd kind of "shewled around" as though they had something to say they didn't want her to hear. She knew the signs. She herself had made so many remarks about people that she knew all about it.

She'd overheard some of the women. "You don't say so!" "Sh! there's his mother."

James! It was James they were talking about. She wouldn't have believed it possible.

"Jennie, I'll ride home with you when you go. I want to stop and see Mary," Mrs. Cleaveland announced. She folded up her sewing. "I'll be ready as soon as you are."

The women in the next room heard her. "Now what's she going to do?" Several of them looked alarmed. "Is she going to make that poor little girl more miserable than she is now by telling her about James makin' up to Saphrony?"

"Saphrony makin' up to him, you mean."

"Don't you believe Mary don't know it already. She's nobody's fool, and a man can't hide what's eatin' him. He'll come around with some other woman's ideas as innocent as if they was his'n, and his wife will recognize the other woman's likes and prejudices. Usually the wife flares up, and then there's trouble. If she has any sense, and she's got plenty, Mary'll just lay quiet. He'll get over it. They mostly do!"

"But who'd have thought it of Cap'n Cleaveland? He's always been so fond of Mary!"

"That don't make any odds."

"I have to laugh at Mary Ann. It ain't her virtue that's offended! She wouldn't care so much if he wasn't so kind of comical with it. She don't like to be laughed at."

"No, she'd rather do the laughin'!"

303

"Well!" Emily raised her voice, changing the subject quickly, for Mrs. Cleaveland was coming. "I never drunk tea or et cookies anywhere that could hold a candle to Hannah Look's."

Mrs. Cleaveland sailed majestically through the room, not noticing them. She put on her bonnet and cape and left with Mrs. West.

"Thank you, Jennie," Mrs. Cleaveland said with dignity, as she climbed down from the wagon.

"You're welcome, I'm sure," Jennie answered, though she had left the sewing circle much sooner than she had intended, for Mrs. Cleaveland had expressed a desire to get away early.

"She thinks I'm going to tell her my side of the story," was the reason to which Mrs. Cleaveland attributed Jennie's willingness to serve her.

If so, Jennie drove on unsatisfied, while Mary Ann Cleaveland went through the front gate of her son's yard and around the west of the house to the side door. She could see through the window that there was nobody in the kitchen, and then she heard Mary singing in the little sitting room. She could see through the raised curtain that Mary was sitting in the rockall, with the baby lying on a pillow and the little girl in her arms, contentedly sucking her thumb and listening with rapt attention to a sorrowful little song. She was looking up into her mother's eyes, seeing the tears there, but not minding them so long as the song continued. Alvida was playing on the floor.

"Hm!" Mrs. Cleaveland said to herself. "They tear the heart out of you with their demands when they are little, and when they get older it's, 'Good-by, Ma, I'm off for sea.'" Well, these were girls. Mary ought to be thankful, though she herself had had more pleasure with her sons.

Mrs. Cleaveland knocked on the door at the end of the song, opened without waiting for a reply, and walked in.

"Oh!" Mary exclaimed, flushing. For a moment she didn't know how to meet this situation. Then, "Excuse me, please, Mrs. Cleaveland. The children are ready for bed."

She put Alvida and Henrietta in the bedroom before they had a chance to get aroused, heard them say their prayers, and then came back. Mrs. Cleaveland was leaning over the baby, rocking her gently. "Pretty little thing!" she was saying.

"Good night Granny," Mary said for Mary Wilder as she took the baby to bed.

Coming back, Mary waited for what might come. Mrs. Cleaveland usually had a purpose for all her moves. She didn't often come to call, and never before had she come at five o'clock. She had the children out of the way—out of earshot, thank goodness.

"Mary, what are you going to have for supper?"

Mary flushed again. She hadn't thought about supper. She had let Sary Ann go to her sister's for the afternoon and evening when she found James wasn't going to be at home. She had fed the children, so that left only her.

"You weren't going to have any supper, eh?" Mrs. Cleaveland said severely. Mary shook her head and smiled a little ruefully.

"Now, look at here. Don't you go mooning around because James is acting unlikely. He'll get over it. Most of 'em have a spell of acting like a fool. They have to go through it like measles and chicken pox. You wouldn't believe it of Henry, but . . . " Well, she'd let bygones be bygones. "Sometimes it's when they get along in life. James isn't old enough for that, though. Sometimes it's because the wife looks poorly, but you look as well as you ever did, if not better, now you've filled out a bit."

"Perhaps," Mary's lip trembled, "perhaps he really loves her."

"Pshaw!"

"She was his girl first!"

"But he took you and married you. He'd have married Saphrony if he had wanted to. He had plenty of opportunity. She was throwing herself at his head. And she's doing it again—making a fool of him. You'd better look out."

"I've done everything I can, Mother." It was the first time she had ever called Mrs. Cleaveland that. Neither noticed that it didn't seem natural. "I've tried the same tactics she uses. I've tried the opposite ones. I even appealed to him frankly to let her alone. It isn't my problem any more. He'll solve it somehow. If he doesn't want to find a solution, I might just as well hold my tongue."

"Now that's as sensible a remark as I've ever heard of in a like situation! And now, if you'd take something into your stomach . . . "

"Would you like to have tea with me?" Mary asked.

"I should admire to. That's what I came for. Set the table in the kitchen where it's handy and call me when you are ready. I'll sit here by the window."

306

She hadn't long to wait. Mary worked quickly, and by this time she was housewife enough to have a good supply of cake and pies and cookies always ready, and there were eggs and meats and cold potatoes that could be fried.

"Now that looks to me like a real nice supper," Mrs. Cleaveland said as she sat down.

"I'm glad you came." Mary found she could eat now. She hadn't thought she was hungry.

They talked quietly, Mrs. Cleaveland telling Mary the news she had heard at the sewing circle.

There'd been some talk about the war, not enough, it was true, to deafen these women's ears to gossip. Some of them thought there ought to be protection. "Why, a Rebel ship could land here and take this island easy as not." Mrs. Cleaveland imitated the way Susan Holmes had said it.

"And I said to her, 'Where would they get the ships? We've got the shipping here in the North.' They're all for buying guns and drilling. Fool notions! And they looked at me as though I was a Rebel sympathizer—account of Black John, I suppose. Do they think I want my sons killed?"

Mary grew white. "James!" she said. "He'll want to go!"

"No!" Mrs. Cleaveland thought a moment. "No. James won't want to go as a soldier, nor Dan'l either. Dan'l 'll go as a doctor, likely. And Sylvene and James'll go in ships. James, especially, can't understand one faction setting up against another. You won't catch James drilling in the Fair Grounds with a rifle on his shoulder.

He'd feel like a fool. But when it comes to the shipping—that'll be different."

"Yes!"

"Time I left for home, Mary. Thank you for the tea." But still there was something unsaid. Mrs. Cleaveland spoke at first as if to herself. "There might be something —some reason he thinks you're holding him, robbing him of some of his manly prerogatives. You haven't . . . " Mrs. Cleaveland looked into Mary's face, "You haven't tried to keep him from going to sea?"

"He hasn't even mentioned . . . "

"All right, all right." Mrs. Cleaveland reverted to her usual tartness towards Mary. "Come from off and think you know our ways . . . " And she closed the door with unnecessary firmness.

She shook her head as she walked down the path. "That's the trouble," she said to herself. "Maybe she doesn't even know it, but she's tried to hold him too close."

59

JAMES spoke the truth when he told Mary he hadn't intended to take 'Phrony Cathcart to Holmes's Hole. And as he drove along he thought, "Dunno but she's right. 'Phrony does somehow contrive to be in the thick of things. Why doesn't Mary get into the fray? She used to. Couldn't keep her sitting at home."

Yes, 'Phrony'd been there at Ma's so long he took her for one of the family, almost. Godfrey! That outburst of Mary's had made him kind of self-conscious. He wouldn't be able to talk in a natural way, now.

He was turning into the gate. Ma would be waiting, ready to ask him why he'd been gone so long, and where Mary was.

"Hello!" he shouted, loud and on the defensive. In a louder voice, "Hey!"

He got out, opened the door, and looked in. He saw no one, but he heard light footsteps on the stair.

"That you, James?"

"Yes."

"Your mother's went on with Mis' Thompson."

"Gone," he corrected with some asperity, glad of a chance to show himself he had no interest in her. Then as she came in sight his tone changed. "Where you bound?" For Saphrony was wearing a new tight-fitting basque and full skirt made of fine tan wool, trimmed with brown velvet that matched her eyes. And on her head was a most fetching creation. "Yellow wheat—well, doggone it!" he laughed. "A hat covered with wheat ears and brown velvet! You been robbing the barn. Now that's what I call smart!"

"I had to fix up a little," she spoke coyly, "because most likely I'll have to go to Holmes's Hole. I'm going to the store first, and if they don't have what I want I'll have to go to the Hole—ride in the order cart, I guess—part way, at least. Sam may take pity on me and go clear into town."

Well, now, there was no need of that! Silly for him to be riding with an empty seat and she poking down in the order cart.

"Why 'twill take you two-three hours if you have to go down with Sam!"

"I have to get those stays before I can go on with my fitting."

"Well, I'm going down," he said hesitatingly, "but I won't be back until late."

"Say, that's fine. I'll have supper at Cousin Hiram's, and you just whistle as you go past, no matter how late."

Well, why not? Mary had asked him merely not to take

her to the Mansion House—but he'd a good mind to anyhow, just to show her. What right had Mary to tell him what to do and what not to do—to try and make him over? 'Phrony would make a stir at the Mansion House with her stylish airs, he thought. But he resisted the temptation to ask her.

"Maybe there'll be somebody else you can come back with earlier." He'd look up somebody when he got there.

The spring sun was warm as they drove down over the old road. The scrub oaks looked almost lifeless; some of them still clung to last year's leaves. But all through the plains the delicate white blossoms of the shadbush were unfolding like lace over a drab-colored gown. And along the edges of the road innocents and early violets were growing.

James pointed with a sweeping gesture, "Pretty!"

"Yes," Saphrony admitted grudgingly. "But I'll be glad when the leaves are out. Winter is so dull!" She sniffed and wiped her nose daintily.

"Is that Mayflowers we smell?"

"Lilies of the valley, I guess."

"Lilies of the valley! I'm no flower gardener, but I know it's not time for *them*."

"No, it ain't, but shut your eyes and smell." She waved a lace-trimmed handkerchief under his nose.

"Lilies of the valley, to be sure." Hm. Mary always said that.

They drove on in silence. Then they began to talk about the people in the village—about the young folks they had known together—young George Athearn and Heman Vincent and Charlie B and Clem West. Scattered to the four winds they were, each on a different ship. They talked of the girls, of the parties.

"Remember how we used to go down to Watchy through the woods?"

Yes, he remembered. They'd gone down in a buggy. Coming back he'd put his arm around her waist, and he had been astonished and a little alarmed at her response. She had removed his arm, but he could feel now that her fingers had clung to his. She was older than he, and he had felt bashful with her. Well, he wasn't bashful with anybody now. And if he put his arm around her waist now he bet she'd like it, as she had grown to like it years ago—before he'd met Mary.

He switched the reins over and took up the whip. Both hands were occupied.

"Don't often have it so warm this early in the spring," James said. "Say, look at that chicken hawk."

"Wouldn't you like to be a bird, so you could fly wherever you wanted to go?"

She held her head up, her long neck stretched back, her throat throbbing slightly.

"You get pretty lonesome, I guess, by yourself so much!"

"Yes," she answered softly, "but it isn't so much the lonesomeness as the longing to do something different—sometimes I don't know what's the matter with me."

James frowned, puzzled.

But Saphronia explained, "I suppose I'm like the boys that want to go to sea and when they go they hate it until they get home, but they always go again."

"Yes, by George, I've felt that way myself!"

312

"And if anybody tried to tell you that you're better off here it wouldn't help a bit."

"No, it wouldn't help. 'Twould make matters worse. Mary tries to hold me here."

Saphronia shook her head. "She doesn't understand!"

And then she changed her mood, but underlying everything she said was the note of sympathy, the need for understanding, the desirability of her presence.

They were reaching the town now. Suddenly he didn't want to stay down at Holmes's Hole for the patriotic meeting. He didn't want anyone else to take Saphronia home. He wanted to talk to her, to listen to her, to smell the sweet perfume she wore.

He let her off at the dry-goods store, "I'll be at Hiram's at quarter past nine."

She flashed a brilliant smile. "That's not too late."

His voice was gruff as he answered, "No."

60

AFTER he left Saphronia, James drove on thoughtfully. He had come down to Holmes's Hole especially for this meeting. It was an occasion on which they were to bring out arguments for the protection of Vineyard Sound during the war. Besides, he wanted to see Captain Gilbert Smith and Captain Holmes Daggett and Captain Ephraim Cottle. They'd just got home from the Sandwich Islands. He wanted to know whom they had met in the Pacific and how much oil they had taken and what ships were going out in the fall. He himself hadn't thought of going out for another year. He had wanted to stay at home and enjoy his family and his fine house. But now he didn't know. With Mary cutting up like this the best place for him was at sea. Besides, with all this war talk men and ships would be scarce, and they'd need all they could get. It wouldn't be so safe any longer, but whalers weren't always looking for the softest places.

And if his ship should be sunk and all hands taken, then Mary would wish she had been more sympathetic. "Guess 'Phrony'd be sorry, too," he said to himself.

Funny how a person comes back to things. He thought he'd grown up and sloughed off all these associations. He thought he was through with Saphrony. And yet she had the ability to talk his language that Mary, try though she might, would never be able to acquire. Mary hadn't been brought up on stories told by his mother and old Mr. Athearn Manter and John Look, as he and 'Phrony had. Mary had a sense of humor, but it was different. He looked forward to the trip back this evening, talking to 'Phrony and listening to her.

He had to go to the grain store for a bag of feed. He'd get it first, stow it in the back of the wagon, and leave his rig at Bradley's livery stable. They'd have to drive home slowly with a load, but he guessed they wouldn't care. It would be cool, but he could keep her warm. He had a good heavy carriage robe.

It was four o'clock. He couldn't very well eat his supper before five, and then what could he do until time for the meeting? He didn't know when time had hung so heavy on his hands. He always had friends in Holmes's Hole, but somehow today he didn't feel like talking to them.

He went into the Mansion House. He'd sit down and smoke his pipe and wait for supper. The waiting room was empty. He sat down with his back to the door.

Yes, he'd always thought Saphrony was cold and distant. When he was a boy, he never suspected the abandon she seemed to have now. He had liked her, and

Ma had liked her, and they'd kind of drifted together until Mary came along.

He shook himself involuntarily. "Law! She can't hold a candle to Mary."

Now people were coming in. There were folks here he'd never seen before. This would be quite an affair tonight. He'd noticed that the town hall was decorated with flags and strips of bunting. Maybe that was why he felt a sort of inner excitement, as though something momentous were about to occur. He hadn't quite been able to fathom it.

He got up and spoke to some of the men. The familiar act made him feel more like himself. There was Gilbert Smith. "Hey, Gib! Set down and have some quahaug chowder with me, won't you?"

"Don't mind if I do, James. The last time I had chowder was three years ago. A good deal has happened since. And there's going to be more. Looks to me as if this rebellion was amounting to plenty of trouble."

"Looked that way to me when I first came home, but you get used to it. Things are kind of stirred up after the comparative quiet of having your own ship and tending to it."

"Well, I hope it won't last long. War tears a country apart."

"It can't last long. Say, tell me what's going on in the Pacific. What grounds you been whaling?"

Yes, James felt more like himself. Other men came in and joined them. The time passed quickly, and James forgot his uneasiness. The blood flowing through his veins was steadier.

3 1 6

"Come on. We'll be late for the meeting."

"I ain't a goin', James. I haven't been home for three years, and I want to see something of my family."

"Come on, Gib. You'll see enough of 'em before long. I came down here a-purpose for this meeting. You've heard they petitioned the town to prepare for adequate defense in case of invasion."

"You don't say!"

"Seems like a lot of foolishness. If the South is so anxious to fight, still they've got to have ships to get here. *We've* got the ships."

"You never can tell, though, James. Some other country's liable to step in."

"Well, we'll hear about it tonight. This fellow from New York City," James said sarcastically, "is going to tell us all about it."

They continued the conversation as they walked along. Then James noticed a stocky figure ahead of them. It had a vaguely familiar look. "Let's overhaul this fellow," he said.

"Why, hang it all, Mr. Almy, what you doing here?"

The men all shook hands cordially. Mr. Almy asked Captain Smith about his command. Had he seen any of the Rebel privateers? James felt out of the conversation. He hadn't been at sea for over a year now.

When Mr. Almy was alone with James he said confidentially, "I've come on a little business, Captain Cleaveland. Combining business with pleasure, that is."

"Yes?"

"Yes. I'm looking for a captain for the *Ann Wynne*."

3 1 7

"A good ship! You shouldn't have any difficulty finding a captain for her."

"Well, yes—and no! It isn't every man will do the trick."

"No, I s'pose not."

"I want somebody that won't be afraid to sail her—give her her head and let her go—take her out of these waters and around the Horn where she can go whaling."

James looked thoughtful. The old gentleman continued as they walked along.

"I'm not a going to have my stock tied up at the New Bedford wharf any longer—bottoms fouling and rotting. I'm going to get them out of there. All this talk about filling up ships with stone and sinking them to block harbors! I don't believe in it. I want to get the *Ann Wynne* out where she can be a self-respecting whaler." Suddenly he turned to James, "How about you being her master?"

James concealed the thrill of excitement that ran through him. He didn't let on that he'd been figuring on it ever since Mr. Almy first broached the subject.

"Likely 'tis about time I went whaling, but I hadn't planned on going just yet."

Mr. Almy went on with details, making them as attractive as possible. "The *Ann Wynne*'s got finer lines than most whalers. I've put on a lot of new canvas and a whole set of studding sails."

"Stu'n's'ls 'll set her right up."

"You ought to be able to stand a chance of getting away from a raider."

3 1 8

At last James held out his hand. "I'll take her," he said.

The rest of the evening meant little to James. Some Abolitionist was talking. James didn't know what he said. He had already formed his opinions on the subject of slavery. It wasn't right to misuse slaves, and some of the folks down South didn't treat 'em the way Ma handled John. It would be best to give them their freedom and pay them decent wages. He didn't see any sense in going to war about it. But when it came to destroying ships— that was going too far!

He couldn't bear to sit here any longer. He slipped out quietly and went to the livery stable to get his horse. The spring air felt good against his face as he strode along.

The stable was dark except for one lantern that sputtered fitfully against a rafter. James shouted, "Ahoy."

A little boy answered sleepily, "Aye, aye, sir."

"Who are your folks?" James asked, pleased at the appropriate answer to his hail.

"My father's Cap'n Swann of the bark *Ellen Knowles*, sir. And I know you. You're Cap'n Cleaveland."

"Of the *Ann Wynne!*"

61

THE night was warm and caressing, settling down like a fleecy blanket, but as soon as James got into the carriage the horse started off briskly, fanning the air about him. "All right, choose your own road," James said, holding the reins lightly. He knew the horse would move quickly going home.

In a month he'd be at sea. He'd like to have Mayhew Look for first mate and that Tilton boy in the cabin. Eben Clark was still at home, though it was said he was going into the army.

The macadam road was left behind, and now the going was slower. The plains were silent in the soft night air, with only the light blossoms of the shadbush quivering like wraiths or like shimmering foam against a dark sea. And now he could hear the ocean beating rythmically against the South Shore.

It wouldn't be safe to take Mary and the children.

With ships being sunk the way they were he wouldn't risk it. But she had her own home, now, with everything shipshape. It wouldn't be like leaving her with Ma. Ma must have been pretty hateful. Mary had had kind of a rough time aboard the *Seconet*, too, being seasick so much. And she'd taken the ups and downs like a sailor. Poor little girl!

She was scarcely more than a girl now, in spite of her grown-up airs and her housekeeping. What pretty black curls she had and bright eyes and a sweet red mouth. "Get up, there!"

Now he was approaching the gate. The horse didn't need further urging. Mary must have gone to bed. The house was dark except for the small lamp she had left for him.

He unharnessed the horse and bedded him down for the night. It didn't take him long.

Now he turned up the lamp and went upstairs with it in his hand, taking care to be quiet, but in spite of it hitting the banister with his foot and stepping on the stair that squeaked. He'd made so much noise she must surely be awake, so he called as he went into the bedroom. "Mary!" And then more loudly, "Mary, are you asleep?"

Then he realized that he'd have to break this news gently. His going to sea would mean something different to Mary than it meant to him. To her it would mean loneliness and worry and fear, while he, out on the sea, would be clear of all this war talk. It didn't seem right.

"Hello," Mary said, sleepily.

"Say, Mary!" He couldn't keep it from her. "Mary, I'm going to sea—captain of the *Ann Wynne*."

"You are?" Her voice was alive now, responding to his mood, to this new feeling of freedom.

James told of his interview with Mr. Almy, talked about the situation, was astonished at her grasp of it, and —"Say, you aren't glad I'm going, are you?"

"Yes, I am, James," she answered honestly. "It's where you want to be."

He looked at her gratefully. "You can take what life sends, can't you, Mary!"

He began to undress, hanging up his clothes, continuing to talk about the possibilities of whaling in the Northern Pacific. "You want to get away from these Southern privateers."

Mary caught her breath. The *Orinoco* had been sunk before she had got around the Horn, but the crew was saved.

He sat down on the edge of the bed to unlace his shoes. He pulled off one, and then as it dropped heavily to the floor, "My Godfrey!" he exclaimed.

"What is it?" Mary was alarmed at his tone.

"I've forgotten 'Phrony."

"'Phrony?"

"I left her at Holmes's Hole. Said I'd whistle as I came by Hiram's. Never thought to do it. Oh, my golly, won't she be mad!" James laughed heartily, his old carefree, honest laugh.

"Why, James!" Mary said with her eyes sparkling, "You can't leave her there. You'll have to harness up again and go down after her."

James snorted contemptuously and took off the other shoe. "*She* can find her way back!"

The room was dark again. Mary lay still, listening to the throb of life within the Island—young lambs bleating, pinkletinks piping up shrilly in the swamp, insect sounds in the lengthening grass, and over all the murmur of the sea. She could not escape the sea.

But tonight the ocean sounded calm and soothing. The salt breeze felt clean in her nostrils; it had bathed away the webs of doubt and distrust.

James was happy now. He would be in his element again, commanding a ship, listening to the wind singing aloft. What a fool she had been not to see it before; not to see it till his mother had spoken.

Mary put out her hand to touch his, and James clasped her fingers tightly and drew her towards him. He put his arms about her gently and his lips against hers.

"Mary," he whispered, "Mary, darling!"

The sea that would take him away from her had brought them close once more.

Appendix

WE HAVE always been impressed with the drama in Grandmother's life and have taken notes at various times and tucked them away for future reference. Then during a trip to the Bourne Whaling Museum in New Bedford we were intrigued with the half-sized model of the whale ship *Lagoda* that stood in the center of the large hall and the various shops fitted out in the balcony. As we stood on the deck of this model and talked to Captain Pierce about his experiences in the Southern Pacific and his recollections of Talcahuano and Paita, we planned to write Grandmother's life and show the heyday of whaling as seen through the eyes of a woman.

So we went to the customhouse there and looked up old records of the ships Grandfather and Great-grandfather Cleaveland had sailed. We looked up records in the library and in the museum. In all of these places the warmth of our welcome and the cooperation of the officials matched our own enthusiasm as we found item after item to add to the growing store.

But perhaps the most pleasing days of research were those spent in the office of the *Vineyard Gazette* in Edgartown. Mr. and Mrs. Henry Beetle Hough, the editors, let us take the valuable old files dating back over ninety years and turned over what was then limited space for our use. In a recent visit to the historic house that is now used for their business office they showed us a lovely period room with old desk and table. "This is the room where you can do your next research," Henry Hough told us.

In that old office we would use a composing table or even the upended roll of paper for a desk, and it was a rare day that we didn't get in the way of the busy printers. There we culled from the files delightful stories or a few pertinent lines that brought to mind or verified some familiar anecdote or bit of family lore. Often a line in the shipping news gave a clue to a dramatic incident that had never appeared in print.

Using these data, we were able to question some of the older inhabitants of the Island and draw out more information. The mention of a ship's name and a captain simply called Cleaveland or Cleveland would lead to a series of letters to customhouses and consulates.

Some of the information we found, with its application to the different books of this volume, follows.

Book I. *The Island*

Page 3. The islanders looked to the sea and sky for weather signs. The sound of the breakers on South Beach might not be noticed in the center of the Vineyard by a stranger, but the native would say, "We're due for a gale of wind." Or, "You can expect a no'theaster by tomorrow." And he was usually right.

On May 14, 1852, the *New Bedford Mercury* stated:
"No arrivals. Wind N.E., a gale."

On May 15, 1852:
"No arrivals."

It must have been quite a storm, for vessels came and went frequently in those days.

Page 7. Black John stands out from the pages of *Martha's Vineyard, Summer Resort*, by Henry Beetle Hough.

"Presently the minister is near enough to see a Negro of gigantic stature striking off protruding branches from the trees with a war sword. The man is, it proves, a servant of Captain Cleaveland of West Tisbury, a retired whaling master, brought to the Vineyard from Valparaíso, and he is using a blade of the captain's."

Page 9. Holmes's Hole is now called Vineyard Haven. It was part of the town of Tisbury. Hole is another name for harbor and is still found as part of such names as Quicks's Hole and Woods Hole.

Page 10. In the New York Public Library we found items that were treasure to us. In some cases they must have been literary treasures as well, for we were locked in a glass room with some of the books and pamphlets as we examined them.

As we were going through Levi Hunt's *Voice from the Forecastle of a Whaleship*, written in 1848, we found a record of the *Huntress*, Captain Sherman, gamming with the *Luminary*, Captain Cleaveland.

"Sunday, October 7th [1844]

. . . At 5 P.M. we spoke the *Luminary*, of Warren, five months from home, with 100 barrels of right whale oil."

"Wednesday the 5th [November]. This day we spoke the *Luminary*, Cleveland master. This was the same ship we had spoken off the island of St. Paul. She had not caught any whales since we saw her there. The Captain came on aboard our ship and spent the afternoon with Captain S. After supper he returned to his own ship.

"Thursday, the 6th, we spoke the *Luminary* again. She had caught two whales, and was heaving them in. This our crew viewed with jealous eyes. They became discontented and discouraged; making free to say that other ships were getting whales under our noses, and that they did not believe our old hulk would get a single fish, if she stopped out at sea till she rotted. They blamed the Captain, the officers, and even kicked the dog, that had nothing to say, one way or the other."

We found an old logbook that had been used by the children, now grown up, as a scrapbook. Every page was covered with newspaper and magazine clippings that had special appeal to a child. We tried the experiment of soaking these loose and found that the paper, made of fine linen rags, and the ink, manufactured to resist the dampness and salt spray of years at sea, yielded the paste-smeared clippings and gave us a plain record. It was written by James F. Cleaveland in 1845 and 1846 when he was second mate on board the *Hopewell*. One of the first entries we saw referred to the *Luminary* and "Father."

The custom of gamming was one of the pleasures of the whalers. Two whale ships would sight each other and get as close as weather would permit. Then the captain of one vessel would be rowed across to visit the captain of the other. They would exchange news and letters, and if conditions were right the crews would have opportunities to visit. It was at this time that conversation was precious. The latest gossip from home would be traded for information about behavior of the whales on the grounds. A gam was a high light in the whaler's life.

Page 12. The *Niantic*, Henry Cleaveland, master, was a famous ship, for it was one of the first to reach San Francisco after the Gold Rush had started in '49. She is mentioned in many books about the forty-niners, and her logbook is still in possession of a member of the family.

In the Cleaveland house there is a large picture, said to be the *Niantic*, painted by a Chinese artist while the ship was in China. This is shown in the illustration. The picture of the Cleaveland boys was taken in California in '49.

George V. Richardson, for several years captain of the Panama-Pacific Steamship *Virginia*, on one of his many trips to the West Coast looked up books and customhouse records concerning the *Niantic* and the *Mary Wilder* and had some of the references copied for us.

In *California Illustrated*, by John M. Letts, published in New York in 1852, there is a delightful reference to the *Niantic*.

"The prospect, at this time [Letts sailed from New York in January, 1849, and is in Panama at this point], of getting passage to California was extremely doubtful, and many returned to the States. During the latter part of April, however, several vessels arrived in port, and were 'put up' for San Francisco. . . . I secured passage in the ship *Niantic* which was to sail on the 1st of May. . . . At half-past six the *Niantic* swung from her moorings, and was headed for the mouth of the Gulf of Panama. . . . In the morning we were running down along the coast of South America, the captain wishing to cross the equator, in order to fall in with the trade winds.

329

. . . On the 12th . . . we crossed the equator, and made one degree south latitude. . . . We then headed north on our course to San Francisco."

Later this author tells of arriving in San Francisco Bay on July 5, 1849, "after a run of sixty-five days."

And still later, "The scarcity of facilities for storing goods had induced parties to purchase ships, which after cutting away the spars, they would head in shore, run aground and scuttle; then connecting them to the shore by piers, and building a story on the upper deck, they were ready for occupation, being less exposed in case of fire, and more easy of access, than buildings on shore. The *Niantic* and *Apollo*, ships well known in this latitude, were thus converted, but have since, together with the city, been converted into ashes."

These notes concerning the *Mary Wilder* Captain Richardson found in the San Francisco customhouse.

"*Mary Wilder:* Brig, 213 tons, James F. Cleaveland, master. Clearance papers, dated June 7, 1851.
Brig *Mary Wilder*, Henry Cleaveland, owner. James F. Cleaveland, master, residence San Francisco."

"Crew list dated June 6, 1851.
Brig *Mary Wilder*, bound for Sandwich Islands.
James F. Cleaveland, master.
Crew: Dan'l A. Cleaveland, born Tisbury, Mass., age 21, 1st Mate. Wm. Burton, b. Philadelphia, cook and steward. Duncan McMillan, b. Boston, seaman. Wm. H. Clarke, b. Boston, seaman. Chas. Fitzgerald, b. Ireland, seaman."

The Friend, Honolulu, among the news of merchant vessels, October, 1850, states:

3 3 0

"Am. Brig *Mary Wilder*, October 5, Cleaveland, from S. Francisco, 20 days."

The Friend was discontinued the following year because its editor, Samuel C. Damon, was in the United States.

Page 14. George Athearn was descended from Simon Athearn, one of the first proprietors of Tisbury and one of the most vital characters of early Vineyard history. "Squire George" was graduated from Harvard in 1775, practiced law, and was judge of probate court for years.

Mary Ann Cleaveland was not much concerned with her ancestry nor with that of her associates. But she was proud of being descended from Simon Athearn, whom she considered a patriot.

Simon Athearn, original pro-   m. Mary Butler 1665
    prietor
Jethro Athearn b. 1692   m. Mary Mayhew 1720
James Athearn b. 1725   m. Rebecca Scudder
George Athearn b. 1754   m. Hepsibeth Hussey 1778
Mary L. Athearn b. 1782   m. Freeborn Look
                             m. Willard Luce 1819
Mary Ann Look b. 1806   m. Henry Cleaveland

Book II. *The Bride*

Page 31. We know very little about Grandmother's early life in Sydney. We had to piece it out from scraps of information.

We have Mary Carlin's marriage certificate dated Honolulu, November 24, 1851. We know that she was in the Sandwich Islands, as the Hawaiian Islands were then called, for less than a month. So when we found from the United States Customs Service at Honolulu that the little brig *Emma Prescott* was the only vessel to make port from Sydney during that time we knew when and how Grandmother must have left her home.

"British Brig *Emma Prescott* made entry at Honolulu, November 7, 1851; Henry Fligg master; 160 tons; 65.23 days from Sydney via Tahiti; cleared November 26, 1851."

The only passengers that were listed, according to information sent from the Mitchell Library in Sydney, were Mr. Lohn, Mr. Moan, and Mr. Cushing. We supplied Mrs. Lohn.

Page 35. The Sandwich Islands were popular with the whalers. They came out in winter, sailing around Cape Horn, stopped at the islands in the spring, then went to the whaling grounds for the summer. In the fall they returned to Honolulu from Northern Grounds and made the Horn in the winter. When the whalers were out for more than one year they visited Honolulu or Lahaina frequently. In 1840 there were eighty-six arrivals at Honolulu and Lahaina, in 1843 there were 383, and in 1846 the number had increased to 596.

Page 57. Grandmother often spoke of the "peachblow silk" she wore when she was married.

Page 61. Years later Grandmother visited her sister Ellen Carlin McCloskey in California.

Page 63. Most of the efficient whaling captains disapproved of a sloppy-looking ship for both aesthetic and business reasons. Captain Cleaveland could not tolerate dirt or neglect, especially when a vessel was making port. Dirty sails were merely one evidence of lack of pride.

On the long voyage home the sailors had plenty of time to clean the vessel and make things presentable. They scrubbed the decks, dismantled and stowed the tryworks, slushed and scraped down the masts, and put the rigging in order. It was customary to remove chafing gear and other utilitarian material to add to the appearance of the ship just before she made port.

This cleaning and mending helped to make the refitting easier, and as a result the ship could be made ready for her next cruise in a shorter time.

Page 74. The *Vineyard Gazette* was full of items about Jennie Lind. On December 15, 1850, the *Gazette* says:

"Mr. Barnum is said to have returned the following reply to the $50,000 offer for Jenny Lind from San Francisco. Mr. Micawber could not have done it better:

'If you would transmute your whole city into one solid diamond, and lay it at my feet as a compensation, I would not risk the health and comfort of the Nightingale by undertaking the tedious and perilous journey!' "

Page 76. Joseph and Eliza Nickerson bought Squire George's property from the impecunious Jimmy Jones, who thus disposed of most of Avis's property.

"The subscriber offers for sale, his property in the village of West Tisbury. The house is well adapted for a public house, and is well built of good materials. A large part of the money may remain on mortgage. It will be sold at a very reasonable price.
                    James A. Jones
West Tisbury, May 21, 1846   3t   "
        Vineyard Gazette, May 21, 1846.

Book III. *In the Village*

Page 120. The parish records of the First Congregational Church gave us information about early doings in the church.

Page 128. "Little Belle" became Mrs. David Mayhew. She lived to be ninety-two and remembered many of the incidents told about the visits to Deacon Cottle's. She is the authority for the story of the muddy bedspread.

Page 133. Letters came by way of other ships that chanced to meet them in the Pacific. In the back of some of the logbooks are lists of letters to be delivered, some of them crossed out as they were turned over to the addressees.

The Whalemen's Shipping List and Merchants' Transcript, New Bedford, September 21, 1852, gives the crew list of the *Mary Wilder*.

"Ship *Mary Wilder*, of New Bedford, Capt. James F. Cleaveland, sailed from this port Sept. 20, 1852, for the Pacific Ocean. The following persons compose her crew:

James A. Crowell	Fairhaven, Mass.	Mate	35 yrs.	L. B.
Henry J. Coop	N.B., Mass.	2nd		D. D.
Abner W. Kempton	N.B., Mass.	3rd	22	L. Br.
Francis N. Mayhew	Chilmark		20	L. Br.
Alfred H. Washburn	Wilmington, N.Y.		22	L. L.
Mayhew Norton	Tisbury, Mass.	Cooper	33	L. Br.
Chas. C. Macy	Lenox, Mass.		27	B. Lt.
John Lytle	Petersburgh, Va.		38	B. Lt.
Benj. F. Maker	N.B., Mass.		15	L. Br.
Chas. F. Ricketson	Dartmouth, Mass.		17	L. D.
Humphrey S. Taber	Fairhaven, Mass.		21	L. Br.
Charles J. Hoffman	Esopus, N.Y.		25	L. D.
Daniel L. Ricketson	N.B., Mass.		16	L. Br.
James Howard	Hardwick, Mass.		29	D. Br.
Chas. F. Davenport	Fairhaven, Mass.			
Chas. H. Andrews	New Britain, Ct.		21	L. Br.
Elijah N. Andrews	New Britain, Ct.		24	L. Br.

Edwin W. Athearn	Tisbury, Mass.	15	L. L.
John Boyle	Randolph Mass.		
Manuel Victorino	Places of residence unknown		
Antone Brazil	seamen		
John Richards			
Martin Johnson			

The initials above refer to the complexion and the color of eyes.

Page 134. The *Vineyard Gazette*, of May 6, 1853, tells of Martin Johnson's being washed overboard.

Page 140. Glowing coals were put in the long-handled warming pan and the lid closed securely. It was then placed between the sheets of the cold bed and moved about to dispel the chill and dampness.

Page 141. Theodor was pronounced with the accent on the first *o*. It was shortened to Theode, with the accent on the *ode*. There seems to be no reason for this name other than originality.

Page 142. The tombstone of Mary Ann's mother, with Mary L. carved on it, stands in the West Tisbury graveyard.

Page 153. The duel episode belongs with an earlier voyage and is related by John Wesley Mayhew Whiting in *The Vineyard Magazine*, Vol. I, No. 7, 1925.

"Captain James Cleaveland of West Tisbury was once first mate on a ship sailing from Panama to San Francisco. It was rough weather and he was obliged to speak curtly to some of the passengers. One of them, an English gentleman, took offense at this and demanded satisfaction. The first mate accepted and being the person challenged had the choice of weapons, so he selected those with which he was most expert—harpoons.

When the Englishman went jauntily on deck and was handed one of these huge irons he turned deadly pale, decided he did not wish to fight a duel at all and humbly apologized to Mr. Cleaveland."

Perhaps this incident inspired Mark Twain's tomahawk episode.

The *Vineyard Gazette*, November 14, 1851, quotes correspondence of the *New York Tribune* from San Francisco, September 15, 1851.

"The dueling epidemic has succeeded the hanging. Our city has produced no less than four of these affairs of dishonor since my last writing."

Page 156. In *Memorial Biographies of the New England Historic Genealogical Society* there is a paper by Richard L. Pease of Edgartown dealing with James Athearn Jones, and there are many local stories about him. This interesting Vineyard character was a poet and writer of promise, and his *Maid of the White Canoe* is said to have been a model for Longfellow's *Hiawatha*. He was born October 17, 1791, in Tisbury. His mother, Susanna, was the daughter of the Honorable James Athearn, and he married his cousin Avis, "Squire" George's daughter.

Though he was a writer and a charming conversationalist, he was unable to keep the family property together. The Cleavelands resented the fact that he sold the old Athearn mansion to Joseph Nickerson, who was not a member of the family.

Jones died of cholera in Brooklyn, July 7, 1854, and is buried in Greenwood Cemetery.

We have in our possession the deed to the old house:

"Know all men by these Presents, that I, Joseph Nickerson, of Tisbury, in the County of Dukes County and Commonwealth of Massachusetts, in consideration of Fifteen hundred and fifty dollars to be paid by James F. Cleaveland, of the town, County and Commonwealth, aforesaid, the receipt whereof I do hereby acknowledge, do hereby give, grant sell and convey unto the said James F. Cleaveland all the following messuages and tenements, viz:—

"The Mansion, lands, and outbuildings whereof the late George Athearn Esq. died possessed, situated in said Tisbury, and lying south of the highway leading from Edgartown to Tisbury, and bounded by said highway on the Southwest, and so to the East by a lane called the New Lane, till it comes to the land of John Manter, thence Northerly, by land of said Manter, to the first mentioned highway; and also five acres of the easterly end of Cases field, so called, being that part of the field which lies across the highway and opposit the Mansion-house; and also a lot of wood land, known as the Fifteenth Lot in the Tacissa division. Together with all the privileges and appurtenances to the same belonging.

"To have and to hold the aforegranted premises to the said James F. Cleaveland, his heirs and assigns, to their use and behoof forever.

"And I the said Joseph Nickerson, for myself, my heirs, executor, and administrator, do covenant with the said James F. Cleaveland, his heirs and assigns, that I am lawfully seized in fee of the aforegranted premises, that they are free of all encumbrances, that I have good right to sell and convey the same to the (the) said James F. Cleaveland, and that I will warrant and defend the same premises to the said James F. Cleaveland, his heirs and assigns forever, against the lawful claims and demands of all persons.

"In witness whereof, I the said Joseph Nickerson together

3 3 7

with Eliza C. my wife, who hereby relinquishes her right of dower in the premises, have hereunto set our hands and seals, this fourth day of July, in the year of our Lord one thousand eight-hundred and fifty-four.

Signed, sealed and delivered in   Joseph Nickerson Seal
    presence of us.   Eliza C. Nickerson Seal
  John D. Rotch
  Wm. A. Mayhew

"Dukes County ss July 4, 1854. Then the above named Joseph Nickerson and Eliza C. his wife acknowledged the foregoing instrument to be their free act and deed.

Before me Wm. A. Mayhew Justice of the Peace
"Recorded July 25, 1854"

Page 162. Daniel Cleaveland studied with Dr. Luce, then went to the medical school at Brunswick, Maine. He also studied under a Dr. McCollum.

Book **IV**. *At Sea*

Page 170. From the *New Bedford Mercury*, September 6, 1855:

"Cleared Ships *Canton*, *Cook*, Pacific Ocean, by C. R. Tucker and Co: *Seconet* (new 399 64 95th tons) Cleaveland, do., by Charles Almy; Br. sch *Franklin*, *McLean*, St. John N. B., by master.

Sailed Ship *Canton*; schs *Angenette*, . . . "

Page 171. "Edwin Williams" was a typical Vineyard way of addressing someone by his first and middle name or initial.

338

"The old Vineyard custom of using people's middle names as their surnames has proved a pitfall to many off-Islanders. My grandfather, when he first came here, was trapped in this way. He entertained a young woman all the way from West Tisbury to Vineyard Haven in the stage by relating the laughable eccentricities of her own father, such as his throwing dishes out of the open window to clear off the table for guests."

John Wesley Mayhew Whiting
The Vineyard Magazine

Page 174. In the *New Bedford Mercury*, of September 5, 1855, we find new publications advertised by Parsons and Company of 107 Union Street. Among them are listed *Harper's*, *Putnam's*, *Godey's Lady's Book*, *Frank Leslie's Gazette*, the *New York Journal*, the *U.S. Railway Guide*. The *Hidden Path*, by Marion Harland, sold for a dollar and a quarter, *Mary Lyndon, an Autobiography* cost one dollar, and Miss Pardoe's books, *A Pretty Woman* and *A Jealous Wife*, were fifty cents apiece.

Page 176. From the *New Bedford Mercury*, September 7, 1855:

"Sailed—Ship *Seconet;* Schs *Wm. P. Cox*, . . . "

Page 176. Whale ships often carried crews with the majority green hands.

Page 177. From *Whalemen's Shipping List and Merchants' Transcript*, New Bedford, September 25, 1855:

"Ship *Seconet*, (new 400 tons) of New Bedford, Captain J. F. Cleaveland, sailed from this port September 6, 1855, for the Pacific Ocean. The following persons compose her crew:—

Mayhew Look	Chilmark, Mass.	Mate	27
Charles C. Adams	"	2nd mate	21
George W. Howard	Porter, Mo.	3rd mate	23
John R. Fordham	Portersville, Conn.	4th mate	37
Timothy L. West	Tisbury, Mass.		21
Robert C. Look	"	Boat steerers	16
Edwd. W. Thrasher	Taunton, Mass.		21
Manuel Francis	————		
Francis Joseph	————	Cooper	
Edwin W. Athearn	Tisbury, Mass.		15
Wm. L. West	"		19
George H. Coxen	New Bedford, Mass.		15
Isaac W. Reed	Dartmouth, Mass.		21
Wm. H. Wallace	Hector, N.Y.		20
George H. Tuthill	New York, N.Y.		21
George Wright	Philadelphia, Pa.		23
Geo. W. Warren	Ticonderoga, N.Y.		23
Wm. H. Hendrickson	Jamaica, N.Y.		18
Albert P. Winslow	New Bedford, Mass.		15
Joseph T. Wilson	Norfolk, Va.		17
Eugene O. Calligan	Jamaica, N.Y.		25
George H. Ellis	Keen, N.H.		23
Wyman H. Tracy	Boston, Mass.		19
Wm. O. Waldron	Tisbury, Mass.		15
Andrew Jackson		Residences unknown	
Jacob Warner		Seamen	
Morris Moriarity			
George Thomas			
Antone Enos			
Augusta Figuera			
and John Mench"			

340

Page 178. When the pilot came aboard he was in full command of the vessel until he turned her over to the captain. He instructed the officers to put the ship under way and then gave directions to the helmsman as to exact course to steer.

The pilot carried the vessel out to a place safely beyond No Man's Land. They usually went through Quicks's Hole, as this was a direct route to sea.

Page 183. Mary never heard a swearword on board the *Seconet*. When she related this one evening, Donald Campbell got up, shook hands with her, and said, "Aunt Mary, you're elected to our George Washington Club" (the equivalent of the modern Tall Story Club), but she insisted that this was a fact.

Donald had sailed on the *Belvidere*, a steam whaler in command of Captain Steve Cottle. There was fine discipline and morale, but an occasional oath. So we've been told.

Page 185. The masthead rings were two rings, usually bound with rope, lashed about the height of a man's armpits above a crosstree on either side of the topmast. Usually one of the officers and a man would lash themselves into these rings and stand there watching for whales.

Boat steerers were fussy about their line. A new rope was apt to kink and this might cause fatal results when flying from the line tub, so every effort was made to remove the newness and the unnecessary twist from the rope. One practice was to tow a log at the end of a new line to soak it and partially untwist it. When coiled it was fed into the tub very carefully in precise coils, with the sun (clockwise).

After the preliminary orders the captain would go to the masthead or into the rigging to keep watch of the whales and to direct the boats. He would relieve the officer and man, who would slide to the deck in time to put off in one of the boats. The captain made use of a waif or signal flag to give directions.

The boat steerer was the harpooner. He was the one to strike the whale, and woe to anyone who interfered with his right! On special occasions, such as this, he had relinquished his place. In case an officer usurped the boat steerer's duty, he was apt to find his boat missing whales more frequently than was healthy for him.

Tobacco was often more valued than money. The wise sailor packed his chest full of plug tobacco wherever he could find room, and then found himself in a favorable position to barter as the voyage continued.

Two irons were used in harpooning. The boat steerer tried to get both of them into the whale. He usually threw the second when the first hit its mark, even if he had to heave it into the ocean. This saved accidents.

For good descriptions of whaling, the original narrative of Captain George Fred Tilton as written by Joseph Chase Allen in the *Vineyard Gazette* is most readable and interesting.

Page 186. The whaling grounds were sections of the ocean as clearly defined to the whalers as the fishing banks are to the fishermen. The latitude and longitude were well known, and evidences of the whales' proximity could be seen when one knew where to look.

Whalers usually cruised back and forth over these grounds with topsails set on the fore and mainmasts. These could be set for a new tack with little trouble and could be reefed or double reefed in case of a blow.

The loggerhead was an upright post fixed near the stern of the whaleboat. The line was snubbed around this as it came from the line tub and passed between the rowers to the bow, where it was guided by a chock placed near the stem. Not only was the whizzing line dangerous to the men, but friction often caused the wood in the loggerhead to smoke. Water was bailed on the wood to reduce the heat and to increase the drag on the line.

Page 228. The mailbox in the Galápagos Islands was located on Charles Island at Post Office Bay. It was a barrel mounted on a post.

Page 238. The story of Len Sanford was found in *Whaling* by C. B. Hawes.

The sayings and doings of the children throughout the book are their actual ones, as told to Mary Carlin's grandchildren.

Book V. *At Home*

Page 264. Sylvanus Cleaveland's daughter remembers living in the old house before it was rebuilt. She remembers the large fireplace that took a cordwood stick, and she recalls going over to her grandmother's to see her Uncle James, Aunt Mary, and the children when they came from sea. Alvida and Henrietta made an indelible impression by riding on the back of a huge Galápagos tortoise they had brought from the Pacific.

Page 267. Before James ever went to sea he was interested in several girls—one in particular whom we have called Saphrony. We do not know any of her characteristics—we doubt that she gave any actual cause for jealousy.

Page 290. We find by the *Tisbury Records* that on March 20, 1861, town affairs were proceeding normally, very little affected by the great events overshadowing the rest of the country. There were notices posted declaring the purposes of the town meeting—all routine affairs such as choosing a fence viewer, a poundkeeper, and an overseer of the poor. A month later, after "The Confederate Traitors Have Chosen War," as the *Vineyard Gazette* of that date put it, there was another story. Leading citizens petitioned for a town meeting "to see if the town will take any measures for self-defense," and for the procuring of arms. James took no active part in these affairs. His chief interest was the sea.

Page 317. The *Ann Wynne* is not a real ship, for we have been unable to find the one Captain Cleaveland commanded at this time. We know that he sailed during the war, that he was followed by the *Alabama* and managed to escape. Years later, when Mr. Ulysses E. Mayhew was getting compensation for *Alabama* claims, the captain said, "Just my luck! I could have spared the money then, and I could use some now!"

We know the captain was at home in June, 1861, because he signed a deed when he bought Manter's Neck from his father. He was marshal of the fair in September, 1861. From a notation on a Masonic card we know that he visited a lodge in Buenos Aires in June, 1863, but we have not been able to locate his ship.

Bibliography

Alexander, Mary C.: *The Story of Hawaii.*

Allen, Joseph Chase, and Riggs, Sidney Noyes: *Vineyard Poems and Prints.*

Banks, Charles E., M.D.: *History of Martha's Vineyard.*

Baxley, H. Willis, M.D.: *What I saw on the West Coast of South and North America and at the Hawaiian Islands,* 1865.

Bennett, Frederick Debell: *Narrative of a Whaling Voyage,* 1833–1836.

Bennett, Thomas H.: *A Voyage from the United States to South America,* 1821–1832.

Bootes, H. H.: *Deep Sea Bubbles.*

Bullen, F. T.: *Cruise of the Cachalot.*

Cheever, Henry T., the Reverend: *Life in the Sandwich Islands,* 1850.

Chatterton, E. K.: *Whalers and Whaling.*

Clark, Arthur H.: *The Clipper Ship Era.*

Coan, Titus: *Life in Hawaii.*

Coan, Titus: *The Island World of the Pacific.* 1855.

3 4 5

Colton, Walter, the Reverend: *Deck and Port*, 1856.
Colwell, James: *The Story of Australia*.
Colwell, James: *A Century in the Pacific*.
Dakim, W. J.: *Whalemen Adventurers*.
Dawson, Robert: *The Present State of Australia*, 1841.
De Marr, James: *Adventures in Australia 50 Years Ago* (1839–1844).
Dodge, George A.: *Narrative of a Whaling Voyage in the Pacific Ocean*, 1882.
Dulles, F. R.: *Lowered Boats*.
Dunbabin, Thomas: *Sailing the World's Edge*.
Edwards, Sereno, Bishop: *Reminiscences of Old Hawaii*.
Eldredge, Zoeth S.: *The Beginnings of San Francisco*.
Grant, Gordon: *Greasy Luck*.
Haole, A. (Bates): *Sandwich Island Notes*, 1854.
Hawes, C. B.: *Whaling*.
Haydon, G. H.: *The Australian Emigrant*, 1854.
Hill: *Travels in the Sandwich Islands*, 1856.
Hohman, E. P.: *American Whaleman*.
Hood, John: *Australia and the East*, 1841–1842.
Horsburgh's *Directory*, 1841.
Hough, Henry Beetle: *Martha's Vineyard, Summer Resort*.
Hunt, Levi: *Voice from the Forecastle of a Whaleship*, 1848.
Kelly, William: *An Excursion to California*, 1851.
Letts, John M.: *California Illustrated*, 1852.
Lyman, Chester Smith: *Around the Horn to the Sandwich Islands*.
Lyman, Henry M.: *Hawaiian Yesterdays*.
Marjoribanks, Alexander: *Travels in South and North America*.
Marryatt: *Mountains and Molehills*, p. 37.
Norton, Henry Franklin: *Martha's Vineyard*.
Peck, B. C.: *Recollections of Sydney*, 1847–1848.
Shaw, Frank H.: *Famous Shipwrecks*.
Soule: *The Annals of San Francisco*, p. 332.

Spears, John Randolph: *The Story of the New England Whalers*.
Starbuck, Alexander: *History of the American Whale Fishery*.
Swift, William S., and Cleveland, Jennie W., Ed.: *Tisbury's Town and Proprietors' Record*, 1669–1864.
Thrum, Thomas G.: *Honolulu 60 Years Ago*, 1913.
Tilton, G. F., and Allen, Joseph Chase: *Cap'n George Fred*.
Verrill, Alpheus Hyatt: *The Real Story of the Whaler*.
Whitecar, W. B., Jr.: *Four Years Aboard the Whaleship*, 1864.
Willams, E. C.: *Life in the South Seas*, 1862.

Periodicals:

Century Magazine, "Leaves from a Whaler's Log," February, 1893.
The Friend, Honolulu, T. H.
Hunt's *Merchants' Magazine*, September, 1849.
New Bedford Mercury, New Bedford, Massachusetts.
Polynesian, Honolulu, T. H., November 29, 1851.
Sydney Morning Herald, Sydney, N.S.W.
Vineyard Gazette, Edgartown, Massachusetts.
Vineyard Magazine, West Tisbury, Massachusetts, July, 1925.
Whalemen's Shipping List and *Merchants' Transcript*, New Bedford, Massachusetts.

Made in the USA
Columbia, SC
01 September 2018